GCSE Edexcel

Physics

Practice, practice practice — that's the key to doing well in Edexcel
GCSE Physics. And that's where this excellent CGP book can help.

It's bursting with realistic exam-style questions on every topic.
All the core practicals are covered too and there are plenty of targeted
analysis questions to test those tricky AO3 skills.

There's even a section of mixed questions which test different topics, just like in the
real exams. You'll find complete answers to every question at the back. Enjoy!

Exam Practice Workbook

Contents

Use the tick boxes to check off the topics you've completed.

> You can find some useful information about What to Expect in the Exams and other exam tips at cgpbooks.co.uk/GCSEPhys-Edex/Exams

Published by CGP

Editors:
Jake McGuffie, Charlotte Sheridan.

Contributors:
Mark Edwards, Barbara Mascetti.

With thanks to Sarah Williams for the proofreading.

With thanks to Jan Greenway for the copyright research.

ISBN: 978 1 83774 002 4

Illustrations by: Sandy Gardner Artist, email sandy@sandygardner.co.uk
Clipart from Corel®
Printed by Elanders Ltd, Newcastle upon Tyne

Based on the classic CGP style created by Richard Parsons.

How to Use This Book

- Hold the book <u>upright</u>, approximately <u>50 cm</u> from your face, ensuring that the text looks like <u>this</u>, not this. Alternatively, place the book on a <u>horizontal</u> surface (e.g. a table or desk) and sit adjacent to the book, at a distance which doesn't make the text too small to read.

- Before attempting to use this book, familiarise yourself with the following <u>safety information</u>:

There are warm-up questions for the trickier sub-topics, to ease you in and get you thinking along the right lines.

The questions are arranged into sub-topics, so you can get exam practice on exactly the bit of your course that you want.

20% of marks in the real exams test analytical skills that come under Assessment Objective 3 (AO3). AO3 skills include evaluating data, drawing conclusions and suggesting ways to improve procedures. The skills needed to earn these precious AO3 marks are easily overlooked, so sections targeting these skills are marked up like this.

You'll have done some 'core practicals' as part of your course, and you could be asked about any of them in your exams. Whenever one of the core practicals crops up in this book, it's marked up like this.

You're told how many marks each question part is worth, and then the total for the whole question.

In the real exams, some questions test how well you can <u>write</u> (as well as your scientific knowledge). In this book, we've marked these questions with an asterisk (*). Write your ideas down in a logical order. Link your points together using full sentences. Include appropriate scientific terms (spelt correctly). And resist the temptation to waffle — stay on topic!

These grade stamps help to show how difficult the questions are. Remember, to get a top grade you need to be able to answer <u>all</u> the questions, not just the hardest ones.

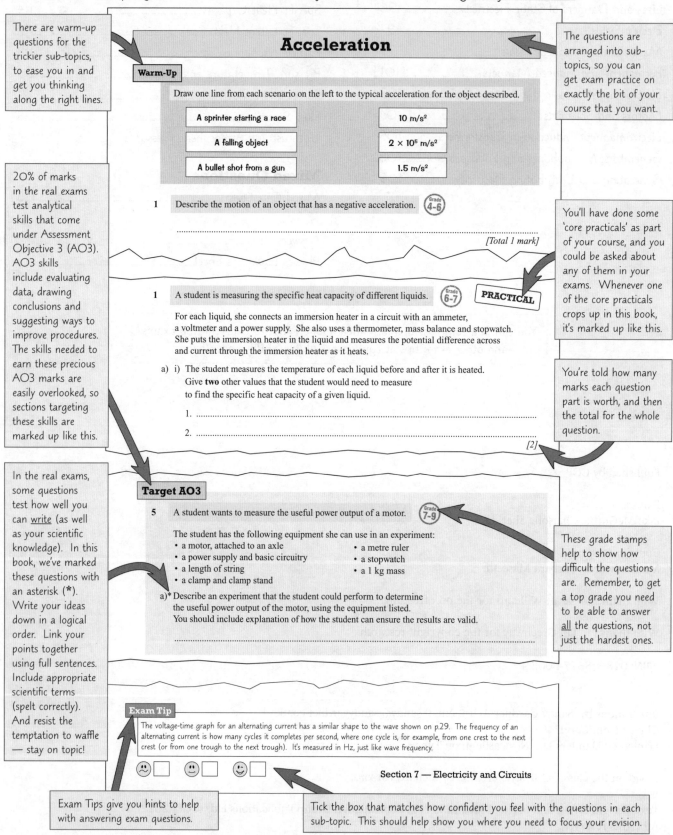

Exam Tips give you hints to help with answering exam questions.

Tick the box that matches how confident you feel with the questions in each sub-topic. This should help show you where you need to focus your revision.

- There's also a Physics Equations Sheet at the back of this book — you'll be given these equations in your exam. You can look up equations on this list to help you answer some of the questions in this book.

How to Use This Book

Distance, Displacement, Speed and Velocity

Warm-Up

Write each word below in the table on the right to show whether it is a scalar or vector quantity.

acceleration   time   temperature

mass   weight   force

Scalar	Vector

1 Which of the following correctly defines a vector? *(Grade 4-6)*

☐ **A** Vector quantities only have magnitude.

☐ **B** Vector quantities show direction but not magnitude.

☐ **C** Vector quantities have both magnitude and direction.

☐ **D** Vector quantities are a push or pull on an object.

[Total 1 mark]

2 The speed of sound varies depending upon the substance it is travelling through. State the speed of sound in air. *(Grade 4-6)*

....

[Total 1 mark]

3 **Figure 1** shows the path taken by a football kicked by a child. When it is kicked at point A, the ball moves horizontally to the right until it hits a vertical wall at Point B. The ball then bounces back horizontally to the left and comes to rest at Point C. *(Grade 4-6)*

Figure 1

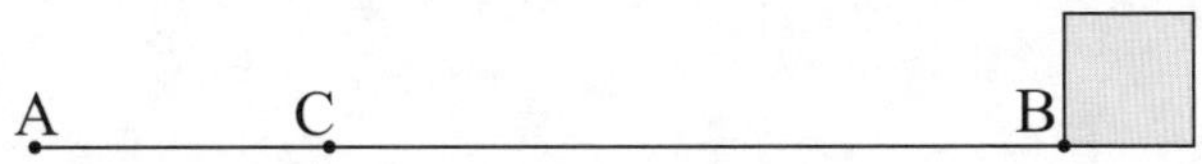

Scale 1 cm = 1 m

A   C   B

a) Determine the distance that the ball has moved through from A to B.

Distance = ... m

[1]

b) Determine the total distance that the ball has moved through from A to C.

Distance = ... m

[1]

c) Draw a vector arrow on **Figure 1** to show the displacement of the ball.

[1]

d) Determine the magnitude of the displacement of the ball after it has come to rest.

Magnitude of displacement = ... m

[1]

[Total 4 marks]

4 A student went for a run. She ran for exactly 22 minutes at an average speed of 4.0 m/s. Grade 4-6

   a) State the equation that links distance travelled, average speed and time.

   ....
   [1]

   b) Calculate the distance that the student ran in km. Give your answer to two significant figures.

   Distance = ... km
   [4]
   [Total 5 marks]

5 A journalist is deciding whether to walk, cycle or take a bus to get to work. There are two routes he could take. The shorter route is along a 3.5 km path that only pedestrians and cyclists are allowed to use. The bus takes a longer route along a road. Grade 6-7

   a) Estimate how long it would take the journalist to walk the pedestrian route.

   Time taken = ... s
   [4]

   b) Estimate how much time would be saved if the journalist were to cycle this route instead.

   Time saved = ... s
   [4]

   c) Travelling to work by bus takes 15 minutes.
      The total distance covered during this time is 7.2 km.
      Calculate the average speed of the bus in m/s.

   Speed = ... m/s
   [3]
   [Total 11 marks]

Section 1 — Motion and Forces

Acceleration

Draw one line from each scenario on the left to the typical acceleration for the object described.

A sprinter starting a race	$10 \ m/s^2$
A falling object	$2 \times 10^5 \ m/s^2$
A bullet shot from a gun	$1.5 \ m/s^2$

1   Describe the motion of an object that has a negative acceleration.

....

[Total 1 mark]

2   A dog sets off from rest and reaches a speed of 3.2 m/s in 8.0 s.

a)   Calculate the dog's average acceleration.

Acceleration = ... m/s^2

[3]

b)   The dog keeps running with this acceleration for a further 6.0 s. Calculate the dog's final speed.

Speed = ... m/s

[3]

[Total 6 marks]

3   A pebble is dropped from a height level with the end of a diving board above a lake.
The velocity of the pebble immediately before it hits the surface of the water is 12 m/s.

Calculate the height of the diving board.

Height = ... m

[Total 3 marks]

4 A boat is travelling at a constant velocity of 5.0 m/s. It then starts to accelerate with a constant acceleration of 0.25 m/s² for a distance of 1.2 km.

a) Calculate the final velocity of the boat.

Velocity = ... m/s

[3]

b) Calculate the time it takes for the boat to travel this 1.2 km.

Time = ... s

[3]

[Total 6 marks]

5 A train travelling at 30 m/s slows down to 18 m/s over a distance of 360 m. Calculate the average deceleration of the train over this distance.

Deceleration = ... m/s²

[Total 3 marks]

6 A cyclist is travelling along a main road. The cyclist stops at a red light. When the light changes to green, the cyclist accelerates with a uniform acceleration up to a speed of 21 km/hr. Estimate the cyclist's acceleration in m/s².

Acceleration = ... m/s²

[Total 3 marks]

Exam Tip

Watch out for questions on acceleration — if you aren't given an equation in the question, you'll have to decide which acceleration equation you need to use. Making a list of the information you have can help, and look out for key words — 'uniform', 'constant', 'increasing' or 'decreasing' might give you a clue as to which equation to use.

Distance/Time Graphs

1   A boat is being rowed along a straight canal. Some students time how long after setting off the boat passes marker posts spaced 100 metres apart. **Figure 1** shows their results.

Figure 1

Distance (m)	0	100	200	300	400	500
Time (s)	0	85	165	250	335	420

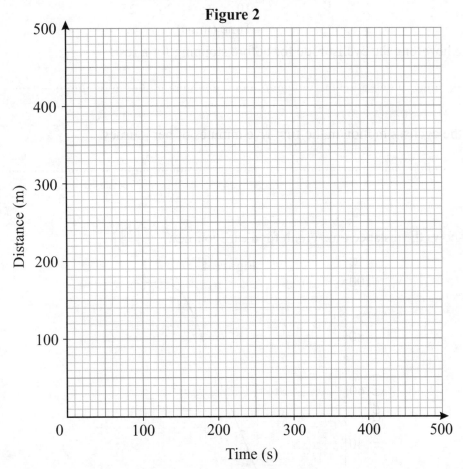

Figure 2

a) Draw the distance/time graph for the results in **Figure 1** on the axes shown in **Figure 2**.

[3]

b) Using **Figure 2**, determine how far the boat travelled in 300 s.

Distance = ... m

[1]

c) Determine the time taken for the boat to travel 250 m, using **Figure 2**.

Time = ... s

[1]

d) The students take the timings using a stopwatch. Suggest **one** way the students can make their measurements are as accurate as possible.

....

....

[1]

[Total 6 marks]

Section 1 — Motion and Forces

2 **Figure 3** shows the distance/time graph for a cyclist's bike ride.

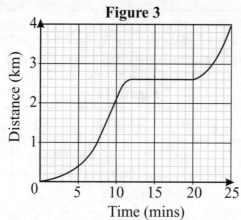

a) Determine how long the cyclist rode for before stopping for a rest.

....

[1]

b) Describe the cyclist's motion in the first five minutes of her journey.

....

[1]

[Total 2 marks]

3 **Figure 4** shows the distance/time graph for a car's journey.

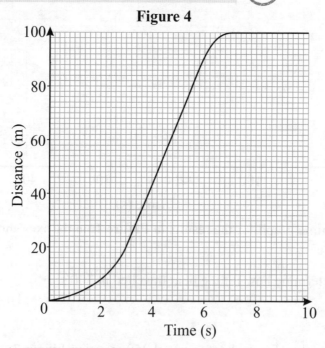

a) Use **Figure 4** to find the speed of the car 5 s into its journey.

Speed = ... m/s

[3]

b) Use **Figure 4** to find the speed of the car 2 s into its journey.

Speed = ... m/s

[3]

[Total 6 marks]

Section 1 — Motion and Forces

Velocity/Time Graphs

Use two of the phrases from the list below to correctly label the velocity/time graph.

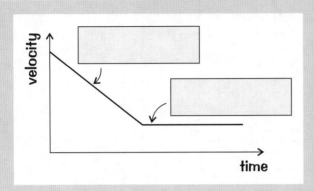

decreasing deceleration

steady speed

decreasing acceleration

constant acceleration

constant deceleration

1 Velocity/time graphs can be used to show the motion of an object.

Which quantity is represented by the area under a velocity/time graph?

- [ ] **A** speed
- [ ] **B** acceleration
- [ ] **C** distance
- [ ] **D** deceleration

[Total 1 mark]

2 A bear runs with a constant acceleration for 10 s before running at a constant velocity of 8 m/s for a further 10 s. Which of the following velocity/time graphs shows this?

- [ ] **A**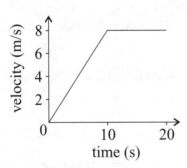
- [ ] **B**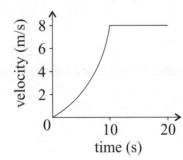
- [ ] **C**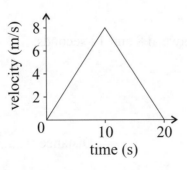
- [ ] **D**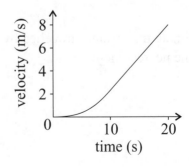

[Total 1 mark]

3   **Figure 1** shows an incomplete velocity/time graph for a rollercoaster ride.

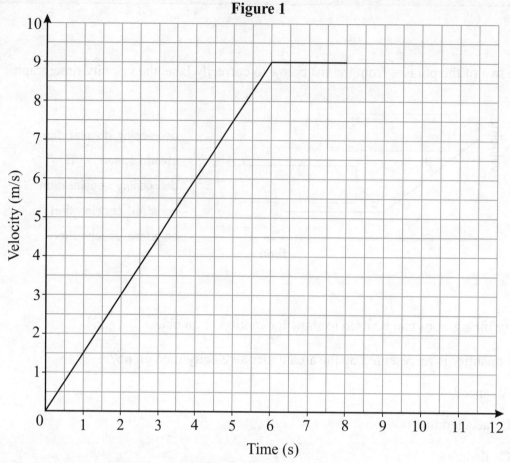

Figure 1

a) After 8 seconds, the rollercoaster decelerates at an increasing rate.
It comes to rest 4 seconds after it begins decelerating.
Complete the velocity/time graph in **Figure 1** to show this.

[2]

b) Calculate the acceleration of the rollercoaster during the first 6 seconds of the ride.

Acceleration = ... m/s^2
[2]

c) Calculate the distance travelled by the rollercoaster between 0 and 8 s.

Distance = ... m
[3]

d) Estimate the distance travelled by the rollercoaster between 8 and 12 seconds,
to the nearest metre.

Distance = ... m
[3]

[Total 10 marks]

Newton's First and Second Laws

Use the words and phrases below to correctly fill in the gaps in the passage.
You don't have to use all of them, but each one can only be used once.

Newton's .... Law of motion says that an object will remain stationary or

moving at .... if there is .... resultant force acting on it.

If there is .... resultant force acting on the object, it will ....

a constant velocity	accelerate	a zero	First
a non-zero	Second	remain stationary	an increasing speed

1   A rocket moves at a constant speed in space. In order to change its speed, it turns
on its thrusters, accelerates to the desired speed and then turns them off again.

Grade 4-6

a) The mass of the rocket is 110 000 kg and it accelerates at 5.0 m/s².
What is the force provided by the thrusters?

   ☐ **A** 550 000 N

   ☐ **B** 55 000 N

   ☐ **C** 22 000 N

   ☐ **D** 220 000 N

[1]

b) State why the rocket continues moving at a constant speed after turning off its thrusters.

   ....

   ....

[1]

[Total 2 marks]

2   A vase is knocked from a shelf. As the vase begins to fall, the resultant force acting
on it is 38 N. Acceleration due to gravity is 10 m/s². Calculate the mass of the vase.

Grade 4-6

Mass = ... kg

[Total 3 marks]

Section 1 — Motion and Forces

3 A sailboat has a mass of 60 kg and is accelerating at 0.4 m/s². The wind acting on the sail provides a force of 44 N. The drag from the water acts in the opposite direction.

Calculate the force of the drag acting on the boat. Show your working.

Force = ... N

[Total 4 marks]

4 A car is travelling at 14 m/s when it hits a wall. It experiences a large, constant deceleration and quickly comes to a stop.

a) Explain why very large decelerations can be dangerous.

....

....

[2]

b) Estimate the size of the resultant force acting on the car during the collision.

Force = ... N

[5]

[Total 7 marks]

5 **Figure 1** shows a 7520 kg lorry. The driver spots a hazard ahead and applies the brakes. The lorry decelerates uniformly and comes to a stop 50 m after the brakes are applied. Estimate the braking force needed to stop the lorry.

Figure 1

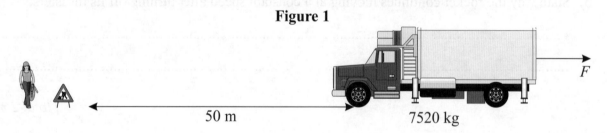

50 m   7520 kg

Force = ... N

[Total 5 marks]

Exam Tip

Watch out for questions talking about constant or uniform acceleration over a distance. They can be tricky with lots of steps. In the exam, use the equation from the equation sheet that links velocity, acceleration and distance to find the acceleration (or deceleration) of an object. Then stick it into Newton's 2nd Law to find the resultant force on the object.

Section 1 — Motion and Forces

Weight and Circular Motion

State whether each of the following statements are true or false.

1) The acceleration of an object in free fall on Earth is 10 m/s². _____

2) The weight of an object is the same everywhere. _____

3) The mass of an object is the same everywhere. _____

4) The weight of an object on the moon is smaller than on Earth. _____

1   An astronaut weighs herself on Earth and on the Moon.   **Grade 4-6**

a) State what is meant by weight.

....

....

[1]

b) On Earth, the astronaut has a mass of 65 kg. Calculate her weight on Earth.
   Use the equation:

$$\text{weight} = \text{mass of object} \times \text{gravitational field strength}$$

Weight = ... N

[2]

c) She wears her spacesuit which has a mass of 80 kg. On the Moon, the astronaut and
   the spacesuit have a combined weight 232 N. Calculate the gravitational field strength
   of the Moon at its surface.

Gravitational field strength = ... Unit ....

[3]

[Total 6 marks]

2   Does a satellite orbiting the Earth at 3.07×10^3 m/s have a constant velocity?   **Grade 6-7**
   Explain your answer.

....

....

....

[Total 2 marks]

Target AO3

3   A student is doing an experiment to determine the gravitational field strength on Earth.

To do this, the student intends to measure the weight of a set of iron standard masses.
Each standard mass is labelled with its mass, which is used as the value of mass in the experiment.

a) One of the standard masses is heavily rusted.
    Suggest why this mass shouldn't be used in the experiment.

    ....

    ....
    [1]

b) To measure the weight of a mass, the mass is placed on
    a small plastic tray that is hung from a newton meter,
    as shown in **Figure 1**. The force displayed on the
    newton meter is then recorded as the weight of the mass.

    Figure 1

    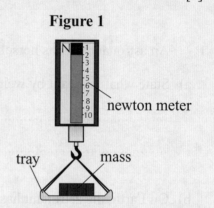

    newton meter

    i) State the type of error that is introduced
        to the results by using this method.

        ....
        [1]

    tray   mass

    ii) Explain how this error is caused.

        ....

        ....
        [1]

c) i) The student carries out the experiment, and records their results in **Figure 2**.
        Plot the student's results on the grid shown in **Figure 3**, and draw a line of best fit.

Figure 2

Mass (kg)	Weight (N)
0.2	2.2
0.3	3.2
0.4	4.2
0.5	5.0
0.6	6.4
0.7	7.2
0.8	8.2

Figure 3

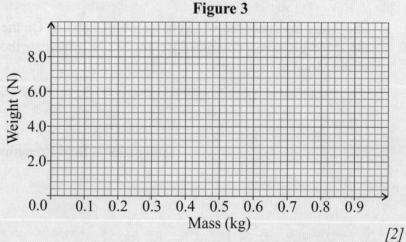

[2]

    ii) Calculate a value for the Earth's gravitational field strength using the graph in **Figure 3**.

Gravitational field strength = ... N/kg
[3]

[Total 8 marks]

Investigating Motion

PRACTICAL

1   A student uses the apparatus in **Figure 1** to investigate the effect of changing the mass of a trolley on its acceleration. The trolley is on a ramp to compensate for friction.

The student records the mass of the trolley and the weight of the hook. The hook has a weight of 1.5 N.

When the hook is allowed to fall, the trolley accelerates. The student then records the time it takes the trolley to travel between the two light gates and the speed of the trolley as it passes through each light gate.

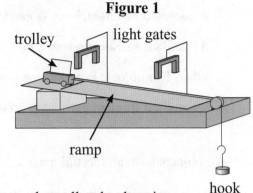

Figure 1

The student repeats this process, each time adding a mass to the trolley, but keeping the hook the same. Every time she adds a mass to the trolley, she changes the height of the ramp so that friction between the ramp and the trolley can be ignored.

a) Give **one** benefit of using light gates to take measurements.

....

....

[1]

b) Describe how the student uses her measurements to determine the acceleration of the trolley.

....

....

[1]

c) i) Calculate the acceleration of the trolley when the total mass of the system is 3 kg.

Acceleration = ... m/s²

[3]

ii) Predict how the acceleration of the trolley will change as the mass of the trolley is increased.

....

....

[1]

d) The student wants to calculate the uncertainty of one of her mean results.
Describe how she can do this.

....

....

[2]

[Total 8 marks]

Inertia and Newton's Third Law

Which of the following is Newton's Third Law? Tick **one** box.

A non-zero resultant force is needed to cause a change in speed or direction. ☐

A resultant force is inversely proportional to the mass of an object. ☐

When two objects interact, they exert equal and opposite forces on each other. ☐

A resultant force of zero leads to an equilibrium situation. ☐

1   All objects have an inertial mass. **Grade 6-7**

a) State the meaning of the term inertial mass.

....

[1]

Three identical shopping trolleys, A, B and C, are filled with different items and so that each trolley has a different mass. Each trolley is pushed with an equal force from the same starting point, and its velocity is recorded immediately afterwards. **Figure 1** shows the results.

Figure 1

Trolley	A	B	C
Velocity (m/s)	1.5	0.7	2.2

b) State which trolley has the highest inertial mass. Explain your answer.

....

....

[2]

[Total 3 marks]

2   Two students each stand at rest on a skateboard by a wall. They both push against the wall with a force of 24 N. You can assume there is no friction between the skateboards and the ground. **Grade 6-7**

a) Explain in terms of forces why the students would move away from the wall.

....

....

[2]

b) Student A and his skateboard have a combined mass of 80 kg. Student B and his skateboard have a combined mass of 40 kg. What is the difference in their accelerations?

☐ **A** 0.3 m/s^2 ☐ **B** 0.6 m/s^2

☐ **C** 1.6 m/s^2 ☐ **D** 3.3 m/s^2

[1]

[Total 3 marks]

☹ ☐   😐 ☐   ☺ ☐

Momentum

1   A motorbike is travelling at 25 m/s and has a mass of 220 kg.   **Grade 4-6**

   a) State the equation that links momentum, mass and velocity.

....

[1]

   b) Calculate the momentum of the motorbike.

Momentum = ... kg m/s

[2]

[Total 3 marks]

2   A car is moving east with a velocity of 15 m/s and momentum 46 000 kg m/s.   **Grade 4-6**

Calculate the mass of the car.

Mass = ... kg

[Total 3 marks]

3   **Figure 1** and **Figure 2** show a Newton's cradle. All of the balls on the cradle have the same mass.   **Grade 6-7**

Figure 1   **Figure 2**

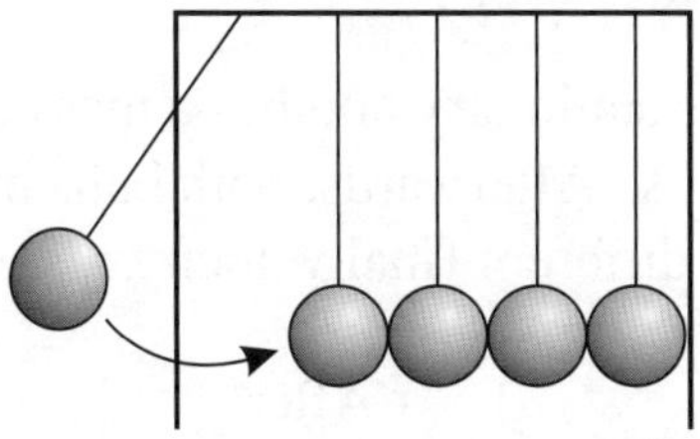

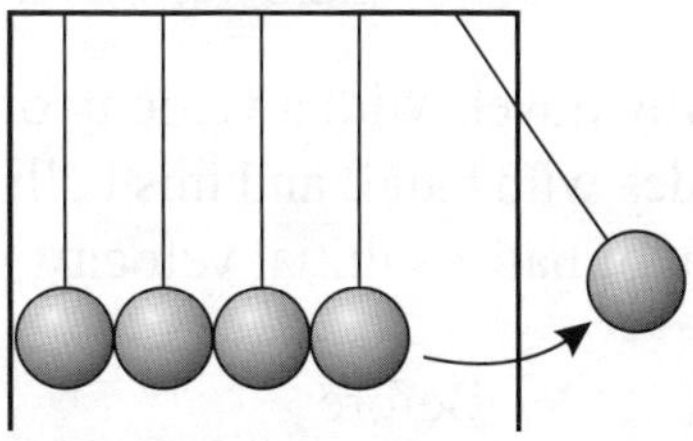

When a ball is lifted and allowed to hit the others as shown in **Figure 1**, it causes the last ball in the line to move outwards, as shown in **Figure 2**. The balls in between appear to remain stationary. Using conservation of momentum, explain this behaviour.

....

....

....

....

....

....

[Total 4 marks]

4   A ball moves with an initial velocity of 3 m/s. It comes to rest after 4 seconds due to a constant resistive force of 0.15 N. Calculate the mass of the ball.

Mass = ... kg

[Total 3 marks]

5   **Figure 3** shows two American football players running towards each other. They collide and cling together in a tackle. Calculate the velocity that they move together with once they have collided.

Figure 3

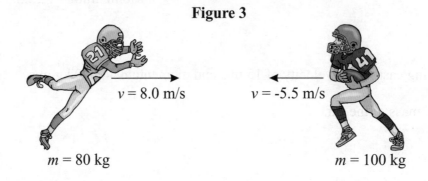

v = 8.0 m/s v = -5.5 m/s

m = 80 kg m = 100 kg

Velocity = ... m/s

[Total 4 marks]

6   **Figure 4** shows balls 1 and 2 before and after a collision.

Ball 1 initially travels with a velocity of u m/s. Ball 2 is stationary and has a mass of 0.2 kg. Ball 1 collides with ball 2 and this collision lasts for 0.1 s. Afterwards, both balls move in the direction of ball 1's initial velocity. Each ball has a different final velocity.

Figure 4

Before   After

Ball 1   Ball 2   Ball 1   Ball 2

v = u m/s v = 0 m/s v = v m/s v = ?
              m = 0.2 kg m = 0.2 kg

During the collision, a force of –6 N is exerted on ball 1 by ball 2.
Calculate the velocity of ball 2 after the collision.

Velocity = ... m/s

[Total 5 marks]

Target AO3

7　A student is doing an investigation into the conservation of momentum using an air track.

The student's experimental set-up is shown in **Figure 5**. Vehicles A and B have equal mass.

Figure 5

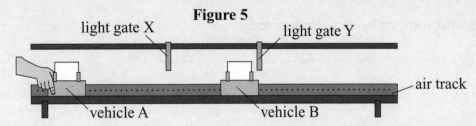

light gate X　light gate Y

air track

vehicle A　vehicle B

The vehicles that travel along the air track experience negligible friction, as they are lifted just above the track by jets of air. The student pushes vehicle A with their hand to start it moving towards vehicle B, which is at rest. The speed of vehicle A immediately before it collides with vehicle B is assumed to be measured by light gate X. The speeds of vehicles A and B immediately after the collision are assumed to be measured by light gate Y.
The student's results are shown in **Figure 6**.

Figure 6

Trial number	1	2	3	4	5	6	7	8
Speed of A immediately before collision (m/s)	0.15	0.19	0.26	0.30	0.34	0.41	0.47	0.52
Speed of A immediately after collision (m/s)	0.04	0.07	0.11	0.10	0.12	0.20	0.19	0.22
Speed of B immediately after collision (m/s)	0.10	0.12	0.15	0.19	0.21	0.20	0.27	0.30

a)　In one of the trials, the vehicles stuck together. Identify this trial.

....

[1]

b)　The student wants to take repeat measurements of the speeds of vehicles A and B for each initial speed of vehicle A. Suggest why this might not be possible with the current experimental set-up.

....

....

[1]

c)　The student plans to repeat the experiment multiple times, while varying the mass of vehicle B. They intend to change the mass of vehicle B by attaching strips of modelling clay along each side of the vehicle. Suggest why the results of the student's experiment are likely to be less accurate as they increase the mass of vehicle B.

....

....

....

[2]

[Total 4 marks]

Exam Tip

For some of the harder AO3 questions, you might be presented with a lot of data. Don't get overwhelmed though. The trick is to pick out the pieces of information that you'll need in order to answer the question and then move on.

Section 1 — Motion and Forces

Stopping Distances and Reaction Times

1 The thinking distance for a driver in a car travelling at 40 mph is 12 m. The braking distance is 24 m.

Grade 4-6

a) State what is meant by thinking distance.

....

....

[1]

b) Calculate the car's stopping distance when it is travelling at 40 mph.

Stopping Distance = ... m

[1]

[Total 2 marks]

2 Different people have different reaction times.

Grade 4-6

a) What is the typical reaction time for a person?

☐ **A** 1.3 – 1.8 s   ☐ **B** 0.4 – 0.9 s   ☐ **C** 0.1 – 0.2 s   ☐ **D** 2.0 – 3.0 s

[1]

b) Give **three** factors that could affect a person's reaction time.

....

....

[3]

[Total 4 marks]

3 A car is travelling down a road, and the driver has to brake suddenly.

Grade 4-6

a) Describe what is meant by braking distance.

....

....

[1]

b) There are lots of leaves on the road, and the road surface is wet.
Explain what effect this will have on the car's braking distance.

....

....

....

....

[2]

[Total 3 marks]

4 The ruler drop test can be used to investigate people's reaction times. (Grade 6-7)

a) Describe **one** other method that can be used to test people's reaction times.

....

[1]

b) Describe the steps involved when using the ruler drop experiment to investigate reaction times.

....

....

....

....

....

....

....

....

....

[6]

[Total 7 marks]

5* A group of friends are driving home from a concert late at night. It is raining heavily and they are listening loud music on the radio. (Grade 6-7)

Describe the factors that could affect the car's stopping distance and safety of the journey. Explain the effect each factor could have.

....

....

....

....

....

....

....

....

....

....

....

[Total 6 marks]

Section 1 — Motion and Forces

Stopping Safely

1   A car of mass 1000 kg is travelling at a speed of 12 m/s. A deer jumps out in front of the car, so the driver performs an emergency stop. The brakes of the car exert a force of 6000 N.

a) The work done by the brakes to stop the car is equal to the energy in the kinetic energy store of the car before braking. Calculate the car's braking distance.

Braking distance = ... m

[3]

b) By estimating the driver's reaction time, estimate the overall stopping distance of the car.

Stopping distance = ... m

[2]

c) Which of the following describes how the mass of the car is related to its braking distance?

☐ **A** Mass is proportional to braking distance.

☐ **B** Mass is inversely proportional to braking distance.

☐ **C** Mass is the same as braking distance.

☐ **D** Mass is double braking distance.

[1]

[Total 6 marks]

2   The stopping distance for a truck travelling at 18 m/s is 45 m. The truck driver has a reaction time of 0.50 s. Estimate the stopping distance for the truck if it were to travel at 36 m/s.

Stopping distance = ... m

[Total 6 marks]

Exam Tip

In the exam, you might need to consider what effect a change in the mass or velocity will have on the braking distance. If the velocity and the force remain the same, doubling the mass will double the braking distance. If the mass and the force remain the same, but the velocity doubles, the braking distance will become 4 times larger, because the braking distance for a vehicle depends on (velocity)^2.

    ☐ ☐ ☐

Energy Stores

Warm-Up

Match each of the following energy stores to the object which mainly has energy in that store.

Kinetic energy store	A nucleus about to undergo a nuclear reaction
Magnetic energy store	A stretched rubber band
Electrostatic energy store	A hot potato
Chemical energy store	A person on top of a mountain
Elastic potential energy store	A toy car rolling along the ground
Nuclear energy store	Two magnets attracted to each other
Thermal energy store	Petrol in a car
Gravitational potential energy store	Two electric charges repelling each other

1   A 0.1 kg toy contains a compressed spring. When the spring is released, the toy flies 0.5 m upwards from ground level.

Calculate the change in energy stored in the toy's gravitational potential energy store when it reaches its highest point. The gravitational field strength of Earth is 10 N/kg. Use the equation:

$$\text{change in gravitational potential energy} = \text{mass} \times \text{gravitational field strength} \times \text{change in vertical height}$$

Energy = ... J

[Total 2 marks]

2   A 0.50 kg rock is dropped from a cliff edge. It falls 42 m before entering the sea.

a) State the equation that links the energy in an object's kinetic energy store, its mass and its speed.

....

[1]

b) Calculate the speed of the rock when it hits the water.
You can assume there is no air resistance and that all of the energy transferred from the rock's gravitational potential energy store is transferred to its kinetic energy store.
Gravitational field strength = 10 N/kg.

Speed = ... m/s

[5]

[Total 6 marks]

Transferring Energy

A ball is rolling along the ground. It slows down and eventually stops.
Fill in the blanks in the energy transfer diagram using the words given below.

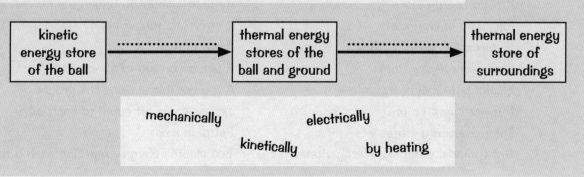

| kinetic energy store of the ball | ·············▶ | thermal energy stores of the ball and ground | ·············▶ | thermal energy store of surroundings |

mechanically   electrically

kinetically   by heating

1   Energy can be transferred between different energy stores.   **Grade 6-7**

a) State the principle of conservation of energy.

....

....

[1]

b) A kettle of cold water is plugged into the mains and brought to the boil.
    Describe how is energy transferred from the mains to the kettle.

....

[1]

c) Describe the main energy transfer for a bike freewheeling down a hill.
    You should refer to the energy stores that the energy is transferred between in your answer.

....

....

....

[3]

d) Describe the energy transfers for a golf club hitting a ball.
    You should refer to the energy stores that the energy is transferred between in your answer.

....

....

....

....

....

[4]

[Total 9 marks]

Efficiency

1 An electric fan transfers 7250 J of energy. 2030 J of this is wasted energy. *(Grade 4-6)*

a) Suggest **one** way in which energy is wasted by the fan.

....
[1]

b) Calculate the efficiency of the fan.

Efficiency = ...
[3]

[Total 4 marks]

2 A student investigates the efficiency of a scale model of an electricity generating wind turbine using the equipment in **Figure 1**. He changes the number of sails on the turbine and calculates the energy transferred by the turbine's generator. The air blower is supplied with 30 kJ of energy and has an efficiency of 0.6. *(Grade 6-7)*

Figure 1

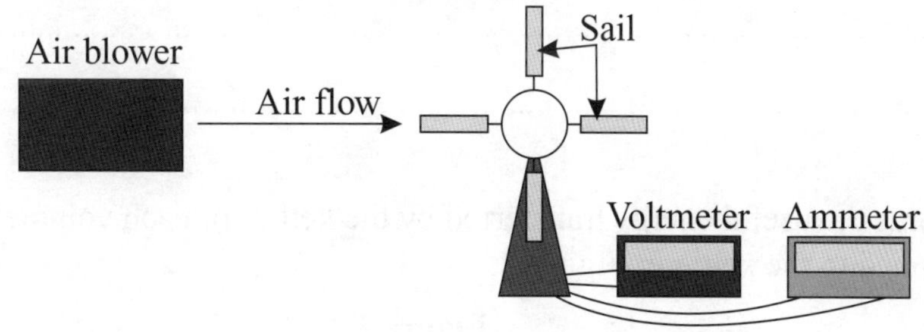

Air blower

Air flow

Sail

Voltmeter   Ammeter

a) When using two sails, the efficiency of the turbine was 12%.
Calculate the useful energy transferred out from the turbine.

Energy transferred = ... J
[4]

b) Describe **two** ways the student could increase the efficiency of the turbine.

1. ....

2. ....
[2]

[Total 6 marks]

Exam Tip

Some of the energy input to a device is always dissipated or wasted. If you're asked to suggest ways to improve the efficiency of a device, think about how energy is wasted and then what could be done to reduce that waste.

Target AO3

3   A student is investigating whether the efficiency of a kettle varies with the volume of water in the kettle.

The kettle automatically switches off when the water in the kettle reaches its boiling point.
The student carries out the following method:
1. Fill the kettle with 500 ml of 20 °C water.
2. Calculate the mass of the water, and calculate the energy that should be required to raise the temperature of the water from 20 °C to 100 °C (the useful energy transferred).
3. Turn on the kettle, and allow it to boil the water and automatically switch off.
4. Measure and record the energy supplied to the kettle whilst it was on using a joulemeter.
5. Allow the kettle to cool, and then repeat steps 1-4 for different volumes of water.

a)   Suggest **one** way the student could improve the experiment.

....

....

[1]

b)   At one point during the experiment, the student forgets to allow the kettle to cool before carrying out a measurement for a new volume of water. Explain how this will affect their results.

....

....

....

[2]

The student records the useful energy transferred by the kettle for each volume of water and the total energy supplied to the kettle in **Figure 2**.

Figure 2

Volume of water (cm³)	660	1000	1330	1660	2000
Total energy supplied (MJ)	0.212	0.302	0.388	0.474	0.547
Useful energy transferred (MJ)	0.168	0.252	0.336	0.420	0.504

c)   Before the experiment, the student predicted that the kettle would be more efficient for smaller volumes of water. Explain whether the results are consistent with this prediction.

....

....

....

....

....

[4]

[Total 7 marks]

Exam Tip

For experiments with a detailed method, take the time to read through the individual steps before you tackle the question. You might also find it helpful to underline key information and data so that you can find it more easily later on.

Reducing Unwanted Energy Transfers

1 A woman is cycling in a race. Before the race, she puts oil on the bike chain.

Explain why putting the oil on the bike chain increases the efficiency of the woman's cycling.

....

....

[Total 2 marks]

2 A builder is trying to minimise the rate at which a house cools.

a) The builder can build the walls of the house using bricks A-D. Based on the information in the table below, which type of brick should she use?

	Thermal conductivity	Brick width
☐ A	High	10 cm
☐ B	High	15 cm
☐ C	Low	10 cm
☐ D	Low	15 cm

[1]

b) Give **one** other way the builder could reduce the rate at which the house cools.

....

[1]

c) **Figure 1** shows the energy transfer diagram for the builder's electric drill. It shows the energy transferred when it is used for 30 seconds.

Figure 1

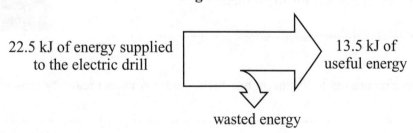

22.5 kJ of energy supplied to the electric drill

13.5 kJ of useful energy

wasted energy

Calculate how much energy is wasted during this time.

Wasted energy = ... kJ

[1]

[Total 3 marks]

Section 2 — Conservation of Energy

Energy Resources

Write the energy resources below in the correct column
to show whether they are renewable or non-renewable.

bio-fuel   hydro-electricity

coal

solar

wind   nuclear fuel

tidal

oil   gas

Renewable	Non-renewable

1   Describe the difference between renewable and non-renewable energy resources.   **Grade 4-6**

....

....

[Total 2 marks]

2   Most cars, like the one in **Figure 1**, run on petrol or
diesel, which are both derived from fossil fuels.   **Grade 4-6**

Figure 1

a) Name the **three** fossil fuels.

....

[1]

b) Give **one** other everyday use for fossil fuels.

....

[1]

c) Some modern cars are made to run on bio-fuels. State what is meant by bio-fuels.

....

....

[1]

d) Suggest **one** reason why car manufacturers are developing cars that run on alternative fuels to
petrol and diesel.

....

....

[1]

[Total 4 marks]

3 A university is considering ways to reduce their energy bills. They are considering building either a single wind turbine nearby, or installing solar panels on top of their buildings.

Grade 6-7

a) Suggest **two** reasons why students living near the turbine may prefer the use of solar power.

1. ....

2. ....

[2]

b) Suggest **one** reason why the university may choose a wind turbine over solar panels.

....

[1]

[Total 3 marks]

4 An energy provider is looking to replace their old fossil fuel power plant. They are eligible for a government grant, so the initial building costs are negligible.

Grade 7-9

a) The energy provider is interested in building a power plant that uses renewable energy resources. They have narrowed their choice to either a hydro-electric power plant or a tidal barrage. Compare generating electricity using these two energy resources, commenting on their reliability and their impact on the environment.

....

....

....

....

....

....

....

....

[5]

b)* An alternative is replacing the old power plant with a new power plant that is run on fossil fuels. Discuss the advantages and disadvantages of using fossil fuels to generate electricity.

....

....

....

....

....

....

....

....

[6]

[Total 11 marks]

Section 2 — Conservation of Energy

Trends in Energy Resource Use

1 The bar chart in **Figure 1** below shows the electricity generated from
renewable and non-renewable energy sources in a small country over 20 years.

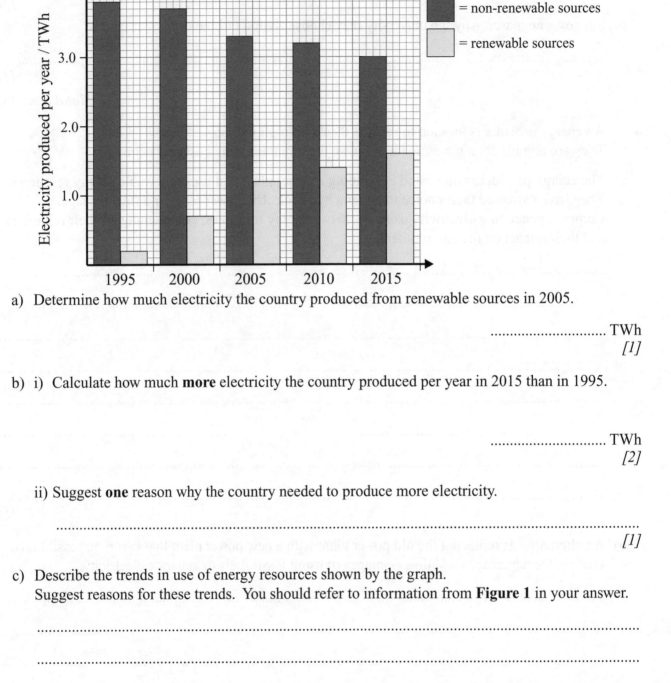

a) Determine how much electricity the country produced from renewable sources in 2005.

.... TWh

[1]

b) i) Calculate how much **more** electricity the country produced per year in 2015 than in 1995.

.... TWh

[2]

   ii) Suggest **one** reason why the country needed to produce more electricity.

   ....

[1]

c) Describe the trends in use of energy resources shown by the graph.
   Suggest reasons for these trends. You should refer to information from **Figure 1** in your answer.

   ....

   ....

   ....

   ....

   ....

   ....

   ....

[4]

[Total 8 marks]

Wave Basics

Warm-Up

Add the labels below to the diagram of the wave.

amplitude   crest

rest position

wavelength   trough

distance (m)

---

1 Which of the following is **not** a transverse wave? *Grade 4-6*

☐ **A** S-waves ☐ **B** light waves ☐ **C** P-waves ☐ **D** ripples in water

[Total 1 mark]

---

2 Which of these is equal to the frequency of a longitudinal wave? *Grade 6-7*

☐ **A** The maximum displacement from the rest position.

☐ **B** The number of compressions passing a point per second.

☐ **C** The number of compressions plus the number of rarefactions passing a point per second.

☐ **D** The time taken for the wave to pass a given point in space.

[Total 1 mark]

---

3 Waves can be either transverse or longitudinal. *Grade 6-7*

a) State **one similarity** between longitudinal and transverse waves.

....

....

[1]

b) Describe **one difference** between longitudinal and transverse waves.

....

....

....

....

[2]

[Total 3 marks]

4 A child throws a stone into a pond. The stone creates ripples when it hits the water, which spread across the pond.

Grade 6-7

a) The ripples pass a leaf floating on the pond.
Explain why the ripples do not carry the leaf to the edge of the pond.

....

....
[1]

b) The ripples have a wavelength of 1.4 cm and a frequency of 15 Hz. Calculate their speed.
Use the equation:

$$\text{wave speed} = \text{frequency} \times \text{wavelength}$$

Speed = ... m/s
[2]

c) The ripples have a period of 0.25 s. Explain what is meant by the period of a wave.

....
[1]

[Total 4 marks]

5 A violinist is practising in a village hall. Her teacher sits at the back of the hall to listen. As she plays, the vibrating violin string produces a sound wave.

Grade 6-7

a) i) State the equation that links wave speed, distance and time.

....
[1]

ii) The violinist's teacher sits 17 m away from her. The sound waves travel at a speed of 340 m/s. Calculate the time taken for the teacher to hear the sound produced by the violin when the student begins playing.

Time = ... s
[2]

b) The violinist then plays a note with a frequency of 220 Hz.
The violinist plays this note for 5.0 seconds.
Calculate how many complete sound waves are produced by the vibrating string in this time.

.... waves
[2]

[Total 5 marks]

Exam Tip

Be careful with units when you're working with waves. You need to remember to convert everything into the right units before you do any calculations, or your answers will come out either too big or too small, and you won't get full marks.

Section 3 — Waves and the Electromagnetic Spectrum

Measuring Waves

PRACTICAL

1 The wave speed in a solid can be found by hitting a metal rod with a hammer, shown in **Figure 1**. The sound waves produced when the rod is struck are recorded by the microphone and displayed by a computer.

Figure 1

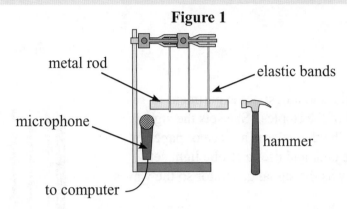

metal rod
elastic bands
microphone
hammer
to computer

A 20 cm metal rod is hit by the hammer. The peak frequency produced was 8500 Hz. Calculate the speed of the wave produced in the rod.

Speed = ... m/s
[Total 4 marks]

2 A student uses the equipment shown in **Figure 2** to investigate water waves in a ripple tank.

Figure 2

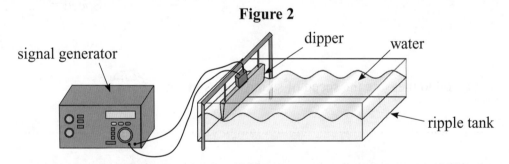

signal generator
dipper
water
ripple tank

a) The student wants to measure the frequency of the ripples. She floats a cork in the ripple tank, and counts how many times it bobs up in 30 seconds. The student repeats her experiment five times. She does not adjust the signal generator between repeats.

State **two** other factors that should remain the same between repeats.

....

....

[2]

Figure 3 shows the student's results. She recorded one of the results incorrectly.

Figure 3

trial	1	2	3	4	5
number of bobs in 30 seconds	12	11	21	11	14

Section 3 — Waves and the Electromagnetic Spectrum

b) i) Calculate the average number of times the cork bobbed up in 30 seconds, ignoring the anomalous result.

Average number of bobs = ...
[3]

ii) Using your answer to part i), calculate the average frequency of the ripples.

Frequency = ... Hz
[2]

Figure 4

c) The student then decides to adjust her experiment to investigate the speed of the ripples. She sets the signal generator to 12 Hz. She then places a piece of paper underneath the ripple tank and uses a strobe light set to the same frequency as the signal generator so the waves appear to not move.

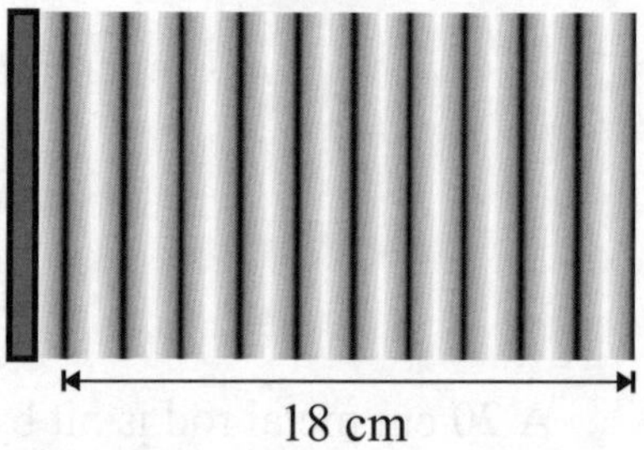

Figure 4 shows the wave pattern produced on the paper.

18 cm

i) Write down the equation that links wave speed, frequency and wavelength.

....
[1]

ii) Calculate the speed of the water ripples.
   Give your answer to an appropriate number of significant figures.

Speed = ... m/s
[3]
[Total 11 marks]

3* Describe a method to measure the speed of sound waves in air. (Grade 7-9)

....
....
....
....
....
....
....
....
....
....
[Total 6 marks]

Wave Behaviour at Boundaries

At the boundary with a new material, a wave can be reflected, absorbed or transmitted.
Draw a line to match each option to the description which best matches it.

wave is reflected	it passes through the material
wave is absorbed	it bounces back off the material
wave is transmitted	it transfers all its energy to the material

1   In each of the following situations, a wave encounters a boundary between two materials. Describe the effects you would expect to see for the following wave behaviours.

a) A sound wave reflecting off a hard, flat surface.

....
[1]

b) A ray of visible light being absorbed by a black object.

....
[1]

[Total 2 marks]

2   **Figure 1** shows a ray of light travelling from air into a clear block of material.

Figure 1

block of material

incoming
light ray

a) What is the angle of incidence for the light ray entering the block?
Use a protractor to accurately measure the angle.

Angle of incidence = ... °
[1]

b) The angle of refraction for the light ray entering the block is 21°.
Complete **Figure 1** by drawing the path of the refracted ray inside the clear block.
[2]

[Total 3 marks]

3 **Figure 2** shows a ray of light travelling from air into glass.

Figure 2

Air   Glass

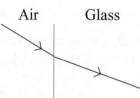

a) State and explain **one** conclusion you can make about glass, in comparison to air.

....

....

[2]

b) Describe how the speed, frequency and wavelength of the light ray change as it enters the glass block.

....

....

....

....

....

[3]

[Total 5 marks]

4 A student shines a beam of white light through a block of clear plastic. The path of the light ray is shown in **Figure 3**.

Figure 3

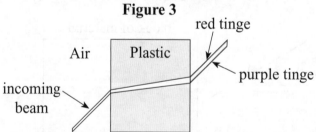

red tinge

Air   Plastic

purple tinge

incoming
beam

The student notices that the emergent beam is wider and is not pure white.
One side of the emergent beam has a red tinge, whilst the other side looks slightly purple.
Explain why this may have happened.

....

....

....

....

....

....

[Total 3 marks]

Section 3 — Waves and the Electromagnetic Spectrum

Sound

1 Humans can hear sound waves between 20 Hz and 20 kHz. One factor which determines the frequencies that humans are able to hear is the structure of the inner ear. State **two** other factors which limit the range of human hearing. *(Grade 4-6)*

1. ....

2. ....

[Total 2 marks]

2 A sound wave hits a boundary between air and material Y. It is transmitted through material Y. The speed it travels through material Y is twice the speed that it travels in air. *(Grade 4-6)*

The wavelength of the sound wave has

☐ **A** increased by a factor of 2.

☐ **B** increased by a factor of 4.

☐ **C** stayed the same.

☐ **D** decreased by a factor of 2.

[Total 1 mark]

3 Two children have made a toy telephone out of plastic pots and a piece of string. The string is tied to the bases of the pots and is pulled tight. A child speaking into one plastic pot can be heard by the child at the other end. *(Grade 6-7)*

Describe how the sound wave produced by one child is heard by the second child.
Your answer should refer to the movement of particles as the sound wave is transmitted.

....

....

....

....

....

....

....

....

....

[Total 5 marks]

Exam Tip

Sound waves can be described in terms of vibrating particles or pressure variations, so make sure you're comfortable with both descriptions. They're a common example of longitudinal waves, so you need to know about them.

Ultrasound

1 Which of the following is an ultrasound frequency? (Grade 4-6)

☐ **A** 3 mHz ☐ **B** 3 kHz ☐ **C** 3 Hz ☐ **D** 3 MHz

[Total 1 mark]

2 Describe how ultrasound can be used to create an image of a foetus. (Grade 6-7)

....

....

....

....

[Total 3 marks]

3 A military ship is using sonar to patrol for submarines. (Grade 7-9)

a) The ship sends out an ultrasound wave and detects a reflected pulse 1.05 s later.
The speed of sound in seawater is 1520 m/s.

The depth of the seabed in the area is known to be 1600 m.
State whether this suggests that there may be a submarine beneath the ship.
You **must** support your answer with a calculation.

....

....

....

....

[3]

b) Suggest **one** way that submarines could make themselves more difficult to detect using sonar.
Give a reason for your answer.

....

....

....

[2]

[Total 5 marks]

Section 3 — Waves and the Electromagnetic Spectrum

Infrasound and Seismic Waves

1 Infrasound produced by earthquakes can be used to explore structures that we cannot see, like the Earth's core.

Grade 4-6

a) State what is meant by infrasound.

....

[1]

b) Give **one** other use of infrasound.

....

[1]

[Total 2 marks]

2 **Figure 1** shows a picture of the Earth. Seismic waves are being produced at point A. Two seismometers are detecting the waves at positions B and C. At B, both S- and P-waves are detected, but the detector at C is only detecting P-waves.

Grade 6-7

Figure 1

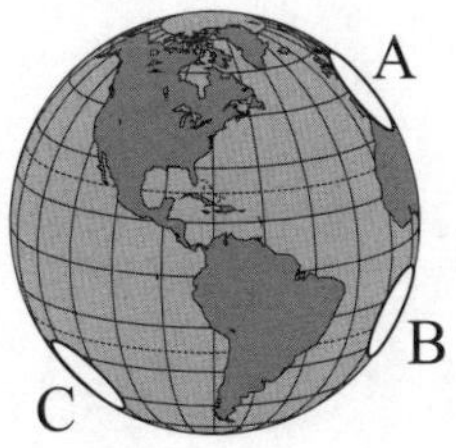

Figure 2

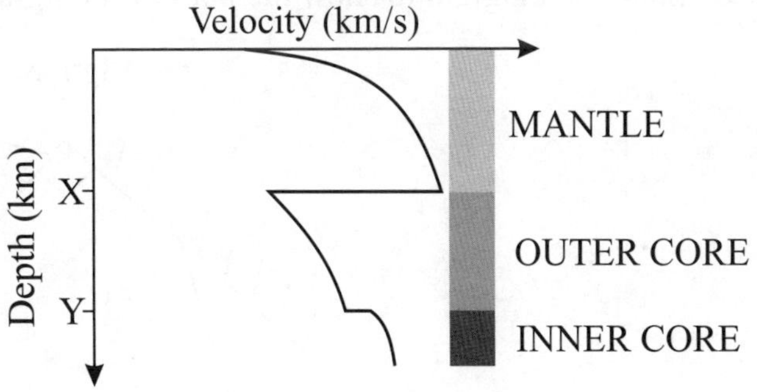

a) Explain how this indicates that part of the Earth's core is made from liquid.

....

....

....

[2]

b) **Figure 2** shows how the velocity of a P-wave changes as it travels through the Earth. Explain why the velocity of the wave suddenly changes at depth X and Y.

....

....

....

....

[2]

[Total 4 marks]

Section 3 — Waves and the Electromagnetic Spectrum

Reflection

1 Optical fibres use total internal reflection to transmit information. *(Grade 4-6)*

   a) All reflected waves obey the law of reflection. State the law of reflection.

....

[1]

   b) Describe what is meant by total internal reflection.
State the conditions needed for total internal reflection to occur.

....

....

....

....

....

[3]

[Total 4 marks]

2 **Figure 1** shows two mirrors that meet at 90°. A ray of light hits one of the mirrors. Complete the diagram to show the path of the light ray as it reflects off both mirrors. *(Grade 6-7)*

Figure 1

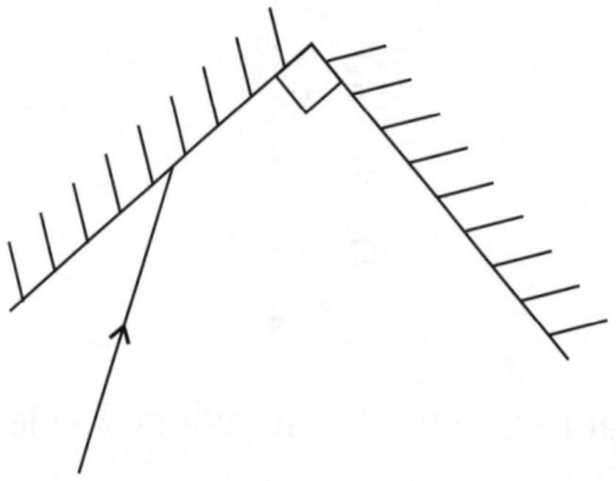

[Total 2 marks]

3 A student was investigating the reflection of light by different types of surface. He used a flat mirror to reflect a light ray onto a piece of card. *(Grade 6-7)*

   a) Predict the type of reflection which was observed at the mirror.

....

[1]

   b) The student observed that the card did not reflect a clear ray of light. He concluded that the surface of the white card was rough, rather than smooth. Explain how reflection at a rough surface would result in the behaviour observed when the ray is reflected by the card.

....

....

....

[2]

[Total 3 marks]

4   A student is investigating the law of reflection. In a dimly lit room, the student shines
a beam of light at a fixed point on a plane mirror from different angles. Each time, they
measure the light beam's angle of incidence and angle of reflection from a line drawn
at a normal to the point of incidence. They use the equipment shown in **Figure 2**.

Figure 2

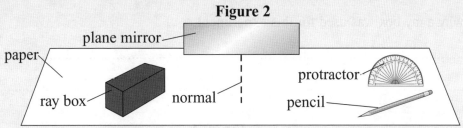

a) The smallest angle the protractor can measure is 1°. The 1° increments marked on the edge of the
protractor are approximately 0.9 mm apart. The student sets up the ray box so that the beam of
light it produces is less than 0.9 mm wide. Explain how this will improve the student's results.

....

....

....

....

[3]

b) The student's results are shown in **Figure 3**.

i) Plot the results on the grid in **Figure 4**, and draw a line of best fit.

Figure 3

Angle of incidence (°)	Angle of reflection (°)
10	14
15	19
20	24
25	28
30	34
35	39
40	45
45	49
50	53

Figure 4

[3]

The student's results don't agree with the law of reflection.

ii) Explain how this is shown by the graph.

....

....

[1]

iii) Suggest what may have caused this error.

....

....

[1]

[Total 8 marks]

PRACTICAL # Investigating Refraction

1   A student is investigating refraction through different materials. The student
uses a ray box to shine a ray of light into blocks of materials at a fixed angle, *I*.
He traces the path of the ray entering and leaving the block on a sheet of paper.

a) Explain why a ray box was used for this experiment.

....

....

[1]

Figure 1

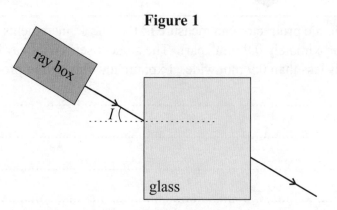

b) **Figure 1** shows the student's investigation for light refracted through a glass block.
Complete the diagram by drawing the light ray as it passes through the glass block.

[1]

c) The student measures the angle of refraction, *R*, of the light ray as it enters the block.
Figure 2 shows the results for a range of materials. Complete **Figure 2** by measuring
the angle of refraction for the glass block shown in **Figure 1**.

Figure 2

Material	*I*	*R*
Cooking Oil	30°	20°
Water	30°	22°
Plastic	30°	20°
Glass	30°	....

[1]

d) State and explain which of the materials shown in **Figure 2** changes the speed of the light ray
the least.

....

....

....

[3]

[Total 6 marks]

Visible Light and Colour

1   **Figure 1** shows some wavelengths of light from the visible spectrum and their corresponding colours.

Grade 4-6

Figure 1

Colour	Wavelength (nm)
violet	430
blue	470
green	540
red	680

Figure 2

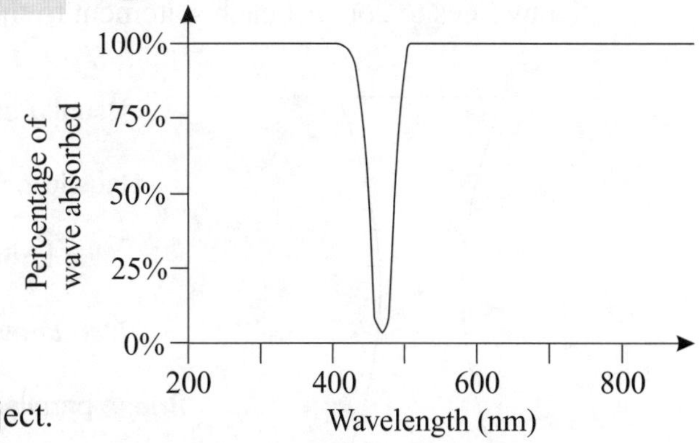

Figure 2 shows the percentage of light of different wavelengths absorbed by an opaque object. What colour is the object?

☐ **A** violet ☐ **B** blue ☐ **C** green ☐ **D** red

[Total 1 mark]

2   A student is investigating the effect of coloured filters on the appearance of different objects. He sets up the equipment shown in **Figure 3**, then blocks out all other sources of light in the room.

Grade 6-7

Figure 3

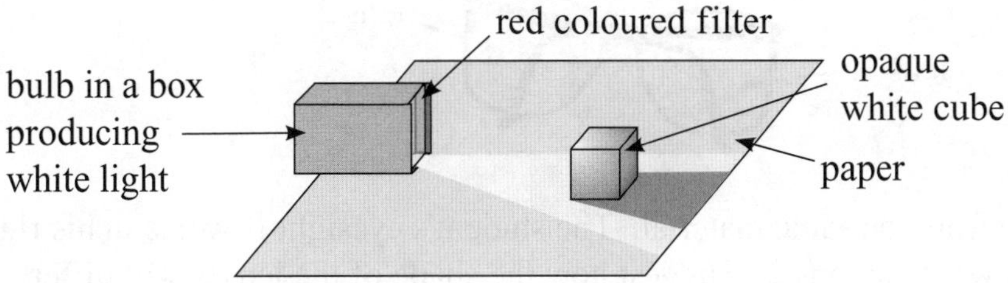

bulb in a box producing white light

red coloured filter

opaque white cube

paper

a)   State the colour that the cube appears.

....

[1]

b)   The student replaces the opaque white cube in **Figure 3** with an opaque blue cube. State the colour the blue cube appears. Explain your answer.

....

....

....

....

[3]

c)   State what would happen if the student were to add a blue filter to the ray box, in front of the red filter.

....

[1]

[Total 5 marks]

Section 3 — Waves and the Electromagnetic Spectrum

Lenses and Ray Diagrams

Draw lines to connect each statement to the correct lens.

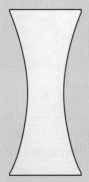

Usually called a diverging lens.

Usually called a converging lens.

Also known as a convex lens.

Also known as a concave lens.

Brings parallel rays together to a point.

Spreads parallel rays out.

1   A student is long-sighted and wears glasses, shown in **Figure 1**.
     His glasses are made from a pair of converging lenses.

(Grade 4-6)

Figure 1

 lens 2

lens 1

a) Both lenses are made from the same material. The student's eyesight is worse in his right eye, so
    lens 1 has a higher power than lens 2. Suggest how the shape of the lenses will differ.

    ....
                                                                                                             [1]

b) Glasses work by focusing incoming light rays to form a real image on the eye's retina.
    Explain what is meant by the term 'real image'.

    ....

    ....
                                                                                                             [1]

c) Images can be real or virtual. Which of the following statements is true for images?

    ☐ **A** Real images can be created by both converging and diverging lenses.

    ☐ **B** Converging lenses only create real images.

    ☐ **C** A magnifying glass produces a virtual image.

    ☐ **D** Virtual images can be seen on a screen.
                                                                                                             [1]

                                                                                            [Total 3 marks]

2   Ray diagrams are used to show how lenses produce images.
Complete the ray diagram in **Figure 2** to show the image of the object formed
by the concave lens. The points marked F are the focal points of the lens.

Figure 2

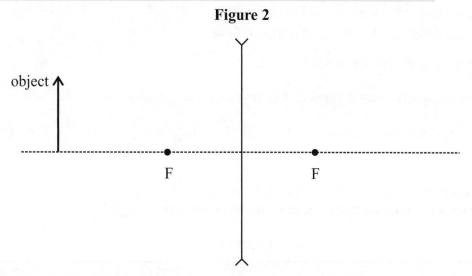

[Total 4 marks]

3   A student uses a convex lens to create an image of a pencil.

a) Complete the ray diagram in **Figure 3** to show how an image is formed by the lens.
The points marked F are the focal points of each lens.

Figure 3

[4]

b) The pencil is moved to the point marked B on the diagram above. Describe how the image
of the pencil will change, including on which side of the lens the image will appear.

....

....

....

[3]

[Total 7 marks]

Exam Tip

You can find the position of an image by drawing only two light rays. Don't spend lots of time trying to draw more.
And of course, make sure that you draw your ray diagrams with a sharp pencil so they're clear and you can change them.

Section 3 — Waves and the Electromagnetic Spectrum

Electromagnetic Waves

For each sentence, circle whether it is true or false.

All electromagnetic waves are transverse. **True / False**

All electromagnetic waves travel at the same speed in a vacuum. **True / False**

Human eyes can detect a large part of the electromagnetic spectrum. **True / False**

1   **Figure 1** is an incomplete table describing the energies of different types of radiation in the electromagnetic spectrum.

Figure 1

Low Energy						High Energy
Radio Waves	Microwaves	....	Visible Light	Ultraviolet	....	Gamma Rays

a) Complete **Figure 1** by filling in the missing types of electromagnetic radiation.

[2]

b) Draw an arrow beneath **Figure 1** that points from the type of electromagnetic radiation with the shortest wavelength towards the type with the longest wavelength.

[1]

c) The visible light section of the electromagnetic spectrum can be split further into the bands of wavelengths that make up each colour. Complete the list in **Figure 2**, which lists the colours of visible light in terms of increasing wavelength.

Figure 2

Red, Orange, ... , ... , ... , ... , Violet

[2]

d) Electromagnetic waves can be generated by changes within atoms.
State which part of the atom can generate gamma rays.

....

[1]

[Total 7 marks]

2   Some types of electromagnetic wave can be harmful to people.

a) Describe how the potential danger an electromagnetic wave poses to a person varies with its frequency.

....

[1]

b) Draw lines to match the types of electromagnetic radiation on the left to their potential side effects on the right.

Infrared		internal heating of cells
Microwaves		skin burns
X-rays		cell mutation and cancer

[1]

c) Another type of harmful electromagnetic radiation is ultraviolet radiation. Give **two** damaging effects of ultraviolet light.

1. ....

2. ....

[2]

[Total 4 marks]

3 X-rays are used in hospitals to diagnose broken bones. (Grade 6-7)

The X-rays are generated by accelerating electrons to high speeds then firing them at a metal plate. When the electrons hit the plate, X-rays are produced.

Staff who work with X-ray machines wear badges that monitor the levels of radiation they have been exposed to, shown in **Figure 3**. These badges contain a photographic film which undergoes a chemical change when exposed to X-rays.

Figure 3

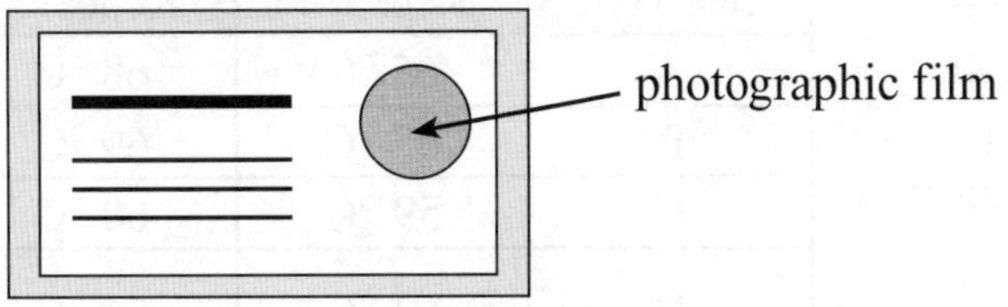

a) i) Energy is transferred when the X-rays cause the chemical reaction in the badge. State the source and observer for this energy transfer.

....

[1]

ii) Describe the energy transfers involved in this process, from source to observer.

....

....

[2]

b) Give **one** other example of electromagnetic waves transferring energy from a source to an observer.

....

....

[1]

[Total 4 marks]

Emitting and Absorbing EM Radiation

For each option, circle the correct word to correctly complete the passage.

Most objects emit radiation across a (broad / narrow) range of wavelengths. The intensity and (distribution / speed) of these wavelengths depends on the object's (size / temperature).

1 An object's temperature depends on how much radiation it is absorbing and emitting.

a) An object is absorbing the same average amount of power as it is radiating. State what is happening to the temperature of this object.

....

[1]

b) Compare the power absorbed and radiated by an object that is cooling down.

....

....

[1]

[Total 2 marks]

PRACTICAL

2 A student uses four identical test tubes, wrapped in different types of paper, to investigate how well different surfaces and colours radiate energy. **Figure 1** describes the types of paper used by the student.

Figure 1
- Matt black paper
- Matt white paper
- Shiny black paper
- Shiny white paper

Figure 2

Test Tube	Repeat 1	Repeat 2	Repeat 3	Average
A	65 °C	68 °C	66 °C	66 °C
B	67 °C	69 °C	67 °C	68 °C
C	59 °C	60 °C	59 °C	59 °C
D	62 °C	64 °C	64 °C	.... °C

The student fills the test tubes with equal volumes of boiling water and seals them with a bung. After one minute, he measures the temperature of the water in the test tube with an analogue, glass thermometer. He repeats this experiment three times. **Figure 2** shows his results.

a) Complete **Figure 2** by calculating the average final temperature for test tube D. Give your answer to two significant figures.

[2]

b) State and explain which test tube has the biggest uncertainty in the average result calculated.

....

....

[2]

c) Suggest **one** way to improve the student's experiment.

....

[1]

[Total 5 marks]

Section 3 — Waves and the Electromagnetic Spectrum

3* Electromagnetic radiation from the Sun affects the temperature of the Earth. Across the day, local temperatures on Earth vary, but the overall temperature remains fairly constant. (Grade 7-9)

Explain how the overall temperature of the Earth remains approximately constant. Comment on how the radiation absorbed, reflected and emitted by the Earth affects its temperature.

....

....

....

....

....

....

....

....

[Total 6 marks]

4 **Figure 3** shows the temperatures of three different stars, A, B and C. **Figure 4** shows how the intensity of the radiation emitted by star A varies with wavelength. (Grade 7-9)

Figure 3

Star	Temperature / °C
A	5500
B	3000
C	10 000

Figure 4

a) On **Figure 4**, sketch a curve to show how the intensity of the radiation emitted by star C varies with wavelength.

[2]

b) To an observer, one star appears white, one appears yellow and one appears red. Suggest which star appears red and explain your answer.

....

....

....

....

....

[3]

[Total 5 marks]

Section 3 — Waves and the Electromagnetic Spectrum

Target AO3

PRACTICAL

5   A student is investigating the rate of cooling due to the emission of infrared radiation.

He is investigating 3 different steel cans, A, B and C, of equal size and shape. Can A is painted with matt navy blue paint. Can B is painted with glossy navy blue paint. Can C is painted in glossy white paint. For each can, the student uses the equipment shown in **Figure 5**.
The student fills each can with 500 g of hot water.
Once the water in the can reaches 50 °C,
the student records the temperature of the water.
He then records the temperature of the water
every 30 seconds, for 4 minutes.

Figure 5

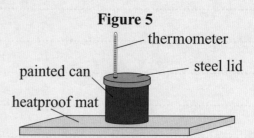

a) Identify **three** ways that the student has made sure
that the results of the experiment will be valid.

1. ....

....

2. ....

....

3. ....

....

[3]

b) Predict the can in which the water will cool fastest. Justify your prediction.

....

....

....

[2]

c) The student's results for one can are shown in **Figure 6**. His results for the other cans are shown in the graph in **Figure 7**. Plot the results in **Figure 6** on **Figure 7**, and draw a curve of best fit.

Figure 6

Time (s)	Temperature of water in can (°C)
0	50.0
30	47.0
60	44.5
90	42.5
120	40.5
150	39.5
180	39.0
210	38.5
240	38.0

Figure 7

[2]

[Total 7 marks]

Section 3 — Waves and the Electromagnetic Spectrum

Uses of EM Waves

Tick the appropriate boxes to sort the radio wave facts from the fiction.

	True	False
Long-wave radio waves can be transmitted across long distances.	☐	☐
Long-wave radio waves bend and follow the curve of the Earth's surface.	☐	☐
Short-wave radio waves can only be used over short distances.	☐	☐
Wireless headsets use short-wave radio waves to transfer information.	☐	☐

1 Electromagnetic waves have a variety of different uses. (Grade 4-6)

a) Draw lines to match each type of electromagnetic radiation on the left to its use on the right.

Ultraviolet		photography

Visible light		satellite communications

Infrared		fluorescent lights

Radio waves		security lights

[2]

b) Give **two** examples of infrared waves being used to transfer information.

1. ....

2. ....

[2]

c) A camper has bought a device that filters and sterilises water so he can drink it.
The device uses electromagnetic radiation to sterilise the water.
What is the most likely type of radiation that the device would use?

☐ **A** gamma rays ☐ **B** ultraviolet ☐ **C** infrared ☐ **D** microwaves

[1]

[Total 5 marks]

50

2   A man uses a security pen to mark his belongings. The security pen contains fluorescent ink which cannot be seen in visible light. *(Grade 4-6)*

a) Which of the following is true for fluorescent ink?

☐ **A** Fluorescent ink emits radio waves after it absorbs ultraviolet light.

☐ **B** Fluorescent ink emits ultraviolet light after it absorbs visible light.

☐ **C** Fluorescent ink emits visible light after it absorbs ultraviolet light.

☐ **D** Fluorescent ink emits ultraviolet light after it absorbs radio waves.

[1]

b) Explain how the security ink can be used to find the man's property if it is stolen.

....

....

....

[2]

c) Give **one** other example of where fluorescence is used in security.

....

[1]

[Total 4 marks]

3   **Figure 1** shows an X-ray image of a skull. *(Grade 6-7)*

Figure 1

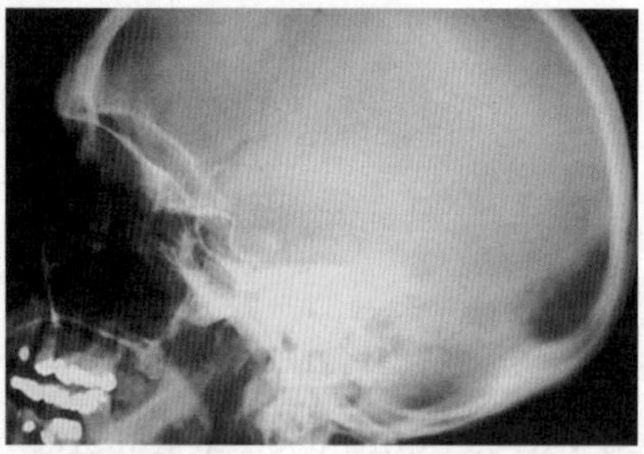

a) Explain how X-rays are used to form images like **Figure 1**.

....

....

....

....

[3]

b) Give **one** other non-medical use of X-rays.

....

[1]

[Total 4 marks]

Section 3 — Waves and the Electromagnetic Spectrum

4 A police helicopter has an infrared camera attached to its base. [Grade 6-7]

a) Describe how an infrared camera works.

....

....

....

[2]

b) Explain the advantages of using an infrared camera rather than a normal camera when searching for criminals at night.

....

....

....

....

....

[3]

[Total 5 marks]

5 A student uses a microwave oven to cook a jacket potato on a glass plate. [Grade 6-7]

a) Describe how microwaves cook the potato in the microwave oven.

....

....

....

[3]

b) The student cooks the potato on the glass plate for 10 minutes. She removes them from the microwave oven and measures the temperature of the potato and the edge of the glass plate. Her results are shown in **Table 1**.

Table 1

Object	Temperature / °C
Potato	78
Glass plate	30

Explain why there is a temperature difference between the potato and the edge of the glass plate.

....

....

....

[2]

[Total 5 marks]

Section 3 — Waves and the Electromagnetic Spectrum

6 Walkie-talkies use radio waves to communicate between each other. When a person speaks into the microphone, it creates an electric current. When the walkie-talkie receives a message, the microphone becomes a loudspeaker and converts electrical current into sound waves.

a) Briefly describe the steps involved for the creation, transmission and reception of a radio wave between a pair of walkie-talkies. You do not need to describe how microphones or loudspeakers work.

....

....

....

....

....

....

....

....

[6]

b)* A family from northern England are on holiday in France. Explain why they are unable to listen to their local FM radio station from back home, but are still able to listen to the same long-wave radio broadcasts as they do at home.

....

....

....

....

....

....

....

....

....

....

[6]

[Total 12 marks]

Exam Tip

In the exams, you may be asked to explain why a given electromagnetic wave is suited to a particular use. So make sure you understand the properties of the different electromagnetic wave types, and know some of their most common uses.

The Model of the Atom

Which of the following best describes the typical size of an atom?

☐ 1 mm   ☐ 1×10^{-5} m   ☐ 1×10^{-10} m   ☐ 1×10^{-20} m

1 Rutherford came up with a new model of the atom as a result of his scattering experiment. *(Grade 4-6)*

a) Name and describe the model that this model replaced.

....

....

[2]

b) State **one** property of Rutherford's model of the atom. Describe the observation from Rutherford's scattering experiment that provided evidence for this property.

Property: ....

Observation: ....

....

[2]

[Total 4 marks]

2 **Figure 1** is an incomplete table showing the relative charges of the subatomic particles in an atom. *(Grade 4-6)*

Figure 1

Particle	Proton	Neutron	Electron
Relative charge	....	....	−1

a) Complete **Figure 1**.

[2]

b) Describe how these subatomic particles are arranged in the atom.

....

....

[2]

c) An iron atom has 26 protons. State the number of electrons in an iron atom and use this to explain the overall charge of the atom.

....

....

....

[2]

[Total 6 marks]

Electron Energy Levels

Warm-Up

Choose from the labels on the left to fill in the blanks on the right.
You do not need to use all of the words.

other electrons   varying

fixed   the nucleus

loops   shells

In Bohr's atomic model, electrons orbit

.... at .... distances

called energy levels or ....

---

1   Niels Bohr suggested that electrons can move between energy levels.   *(Grade 4-6)*

a) Describe how an inner electron can move between energy levels.

....

....

....

[2]

b) State the name of the type of particle created when an atom loses or gains outer electrons.

....

[1]

c) State the relative charge on the particle if it is created by an atom losing an outer electron.

....

[1]

[Total 4 marks]

---

2   A scientist is investigating the radiation emitted from a hydrogen discharge lamp. Inside the lamp, electrons in hydrogen atoms are constantly being excited to higher energy levels and then falling to lower levels. He finds that excited electrons falling back to the first energy level release ultraviolet radiation (frequency $\sim 3 \times 10^{15}$ Hz). Excited electrons falling back to the second energy level release visible light (frequency $\sim 5 \times 10^{14}$ Hz).   *(Grade 7-9)*

Explain why electrons falling to the first energy level of hydrogen release electromagnetic radiation with a higher frequency than those falling to the second energy level.

....

....

....

....

....

....

[Total 4 marks]

Isotopes and Nuclear Radiation

The standard notation used to represent atoms is shown. Use the words below to correctly fill in the labels. You don't have to use every phrase, but each phrase can only be used once.

electron number

neutron number

mass number

element symbol

charge   atomic number

1   **Figure 1** shows a smoke detector. Smoke detectors contain radioactive isotopes. These isotopes are unstable and undergo radioactive decay to become more stable. They do this by emitting nuclear radiation.

Grade 4-6

Figure 1

a) State what is meant by isotopes of an element.

....

....

[2]

b) Some nuclear radiation is ionising.
State **three** types of ionising radiation emitted by radioactive decay.

....

....

[3]

c) The unstable isotope in the smoke detector releases a particle made up of two protons and two neutrons from its nucleus.

i) State the name of this type of decay.

....

[1]

ii) State and explain the range in air of the released particle.

....

....

[2]

[Total 8 marks]

2   A student carries out an experiment to investigate two different radioactive sources. Her experiment is shown in **Figure 2**. She changes the material between the source and the Geiger-Muller tube and measures the count rate. **Figure 3** shows her results.

Figure 2

20 cm

opening

radiation

lead box containing source

5 cm thick sheet of material

Geiger-Muller tube

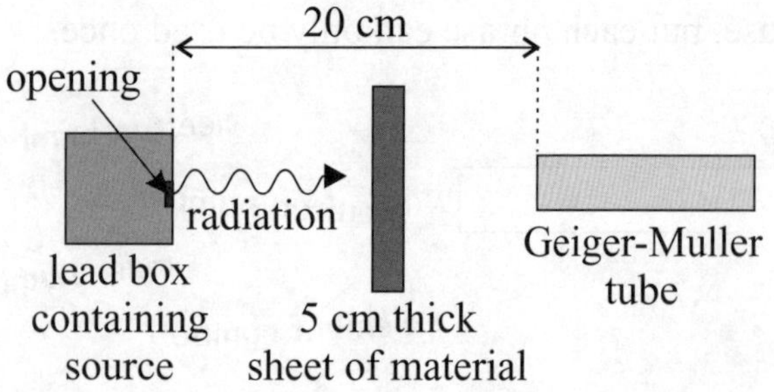

Figure 3

Material	Count rate (counts per minute)	
	Source A	Source B
No material	854	1203
Paper	847	1200
Aluminium	6	1199
Lead	5	280

a) Deduce the type of radiation source A emits.

....

[1]

b) State what kind of radiation source B emits. Explain your answer.

....

....

....

[3]

[Total 4 marks]

3   One isotope of sodium is $^{23}_{11}$Na.   Grade 6-7

a) Write down the nucleon number of this isotope.

....

[1]

b) Calculate the number of neutrons in the sodium nucleus.

Number of neutrons = ...

[1]

c) Which of the following is another isotope of sodium?

☐ **A** $^{11}_{23}$Na   ☐ **B** $^{11}_{24}$Na   ☐ **C** $^{23}_{12}$Na   ☐ **D** $^{24}_{11}$Na

[1]

d) An isotope of neon is $^{23}_{10}$Ne. State whether or not the charge on the neon isotope's nucleus is different to the charge on the nucleus of the sodium isotope. Explain your answer.

....

....

....

[2]

[Total 5 marks]

Target AO3

4　An engineer is investigating how the thickness of paper placed between a source of beta radiation and a detector affects the amount of radiation that reaches the detector.

The engineer uses a Geiger-Muller tube to measure the amount of radiation emitted from the source that makes it through different thicknesses of paper. The Geiger-Muller tube measures the count-rate in counts per second (cps). The results of the engineer's experiment are recorded in **Figure 4**.

Figure 4

thickness of paper (mm)	count-rate detected (cps)				
	Trial 1	Trial 2	Trial 3	Mean (to nearest whole number)	Uncertainty (cps)
0.2	161	157	169	162	6.0
0.3	145	150	136	144	7.0
0.4	129	122	142	131	10.0
0.5	99	122	105	109	....
0.6	93	95	98	....	2.5
0.7	85	89	81	85	4.0
0.8	67	69	74	70	3.5

a)　Complete **Figure 4** by filling in the missing values.

[2]

b)　The engineer states that the count-rate data recorded for 0.6 mm thick paper is the most precise and the most accurate data. State and explain whether the engineer is correct.

....

....

....

[2]

c)　Write a conclusion for the engineer's experiment based on the data in **Figure 4**.

....

....

[1]

d)　The half-life of a radioactive substance is equal to the time taken for the count-rate from the substance to reduce to half its initial value. Explain why it is important that the source of beta radiation used in this experiment has a half-life that is much longer than the duration of the experiment.

....

....

....

[2]

[Total 7 marks]

Section 4 — Radioactivity

Nuclear Equations

An isotope emits an alpha particle. Circle the correct options in the sentences below to describe how the isotope's atomic number and mass number changes.

The atomic number (increases / decreases) by (one / two).

The mass number (increases / decreases) by (one / four).

1 An electron is emitted from a nucleus. (Grade 4-6)

a) State the effect this has on the charge of the nucleus.

....

[1]

b) After emitting the electron, the atom is excited. The atom releases its excess energy in the form of a gamma ray. Describe what, if any, effect this has on the charge and mass of the nucleus.

....

[1]

[Total 2 marks]

2 A student writes down the following nuclear decay equation: $^{234}_{90}\text{Th} \longrightarrow ^{234}_{91}\text{Pa} + ^{0}_{0}\gamma$ (Grade 7-9)

a) Explain why this equation must be incorrect.

....

[1]

b) The student has missed out a particle from this decay equation.
Write down this particle as it would appear in a decay equation.

....

[1]

c) Radium (Ra) has atomic number 88. The isotope radium-226 undergoes alpha decay to form radon (Rn). Write a nuclear equation to show this decay.

....

[3]

d) The radon isotope then undergoes alpha decay to form an isotope of polonium (Po), which undergoes alpha decay to form an isotope of lead (Pb).
Calculate the number of neutrons in the nucleus of this lead isotope.

Number of neutrons = ...

[3]

[Total 8 marks]

Half-life

1 Each time an unstable nuclei in a sample decays, a 'count' is registered by a radiation detector. **Figure 1** shows how the count-rate of a radioactive sample changes over time, after background radiation has been taken into account.

Grade 4-6

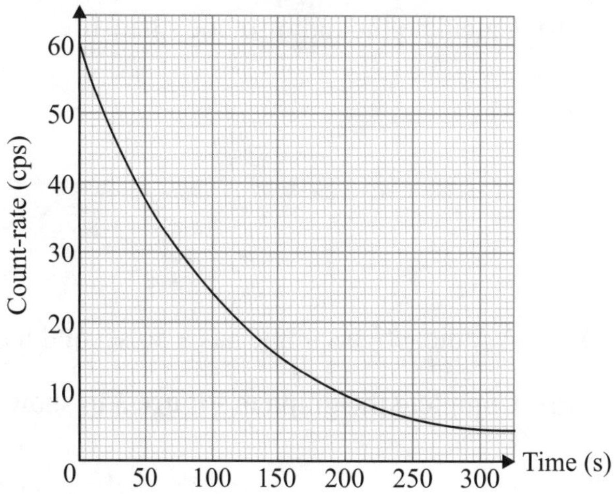

a) State what is meant by half-life. Your answer should refer to the number of undecayed nuclei.

   ....

   ....
   [1]

b) Determine, using **Figure 1**, the half-life of the sample.

   Half-life = ... s
   [1]

Figure 1

c) Initially, the sample contains approximately 800 undecayed nuclei.
   Predict how many of these nuclei will have decayed after two half-lives.

   Number of decayed nuclei = ...
   [2]

d) After two half-lives, what is the ratio of the number of undecayed nuclei left to the initial number of undecayed nuclei?

   ☐ **A** 1:2   ☐ **B** 2:1   ☐ **C** 1:4   ☐ **D** 4:1
   [1]

   [Total 5 marks]

2 **Figure 2** shows data about two radioactive sources. *Grade 6-7*

Figure 2

	Isotope 1	Isotope 2	Isotope 3
Number of undecayed nuclei	20 000	20 000	20 000
Half-life	4 minutes	72 years	5 years

a) State the isotope that is the most unstable.

   ....

   [1]

b) Explain which isotope will have the highest activity initially.

   ....

   ....
   [2]

   [Total 3 marks]

Section 4 — Radioactivity

3 The activity of a radioisotope is 8800 Bq. Six hours later, the activity has fallen to 1100 Bq. Grade 6-7

a) Calculate how many half-lives have passed during the six hours.

Number of half-lives = ...

[3]

b) Calculate the radioisotope's half-life.

Half-life = ... hour(s)

[1]

[Total 4 marks]

4 A radioactive sample has a 50 second half-life. The initial activity of the sample is 120 Bq. Grade 7-9

a) Complete the graph in **Figure 3** to show how the activity will change in the first 150 seconds.

Figure 3

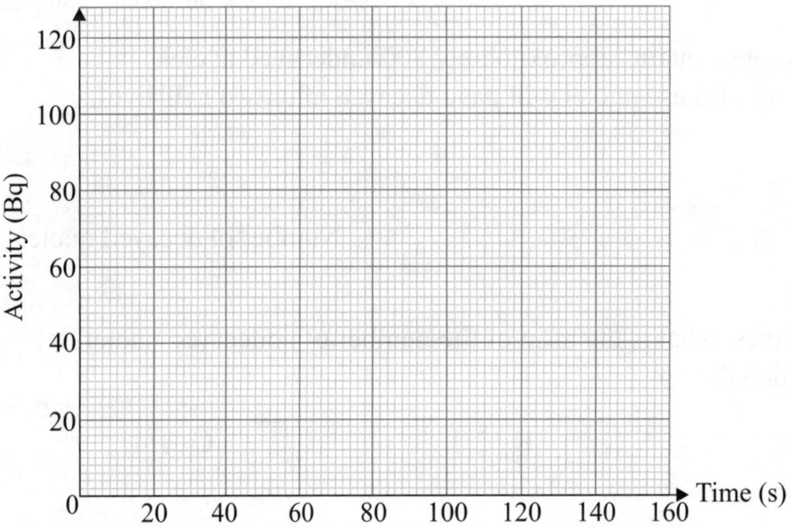

[2]

b) Predict, using your graph in **Figure 3**, the activity of the sample after 40 seconds.

Activity = ... Bq

[1]

c) Estimate the activity after 200 s. Give your answer to one significant figure.
Explain why this estimate is less likely to be correct than your prediction in part b).

....

....

....

[4]

[Total 7 marks]

Exam Tip

Half-life and activity are really important things to get your head around — they're a key thing to mention when talking about any radioactive substance. Remember that every activity-time graph showing radioactive decay has the same shape — radioactive decay is a random process, but by looking at lots of nuclei you can make fairly accurate estimates.

Background Radiation and Contamination

1 Name **two** sources of background radiation. *(Grade 4-6)*

1. ....

2. ....

[Total 2 marks]

2 A scientist is reviewing the safety procedures to be used in her lab. She is concerned about **contamination** and **irradiation**. *(Grade 6-7)*

a) Explain the difference between contamination and irradiation.

....

....

....

....

[2]

b) The scientist is using a low activity radioactive sample. Give **one** example of how she can protect herself from irradiation and **one** example of how she can protect herself from contamination.

Irradiation: ....

Contamination: ....

[2]

[Total 4 marks]

3* Radium-226 is an alpha source that was used in clocks until the 1960s to make the hands and numbers glow. Discuss whether a clockmaker should be more concerned about irradiation or contamination when repairing old clocks that contain radium. *(Grade 7-9)*

....

....

....

....

....

....

....

....

....

....

....

[Total 6 marks]

Target AO3

4 A scientist is carrying out an experiment to find the half-life of a radioactive substance. Before bringing the radioactive substance into the laboratory, the scientist needs to measure the background radiation count-rate in the laboratory.

Grade 7-9

a) A student was doing an experiment using a radioactive source in the same laboratory. The scientist waited for the student to finish their experiment and fully clear away their equipment before measuring the background radiation. Explain how this will improve the accuracy of the scientist's measurements.

....

....

[1]

b) To measure the background radiation, the scientist measures the total counts detected by a Geiger-Muller tube and counter over 5 minutes. She repeats this measurement twice more, and records her results in **Figure 1**. Use the data in **Figure 1** to calculate the mean count-rate due to background radiation, in counts per second (cps).

Figure 1

Trial	Total counts in 5 mins
1	598
2	641
3	624

mean count-rate = ... cps

[3]

c) The scientist records the count-rate from the radioactive substance every 5 minutes using the equipment in **Figure 2**.

Figure 2

radioactive substance   Geiger-Muller tube

0.50 m   detector

Halfway through the experiment, the Geiger-Muller tube was knocked off the bench, and needed to be put back into place.

i) Suggest **one** safety precaution the scientist should take when replacing the Geiger-Muller tube.

....

....

[1]

ii) When the scientist replaces the Geiger-Muller tube, she places it 30 cm away from the source. Explain how this will affect the validity of the scientist's results.

....

....

....

[2]

[Total 7 marks]

Section 4 — Radioactivity

Uses of Radiation

Use the words in the box to fill in the gaps in the sentences below. Not all of the words in the box are used in the sentences and some of the words are used more than once.

Positron-emitting isotopes are attached to substances that are used by the body.

These substances are then either swallowed by or injected into the patient and act as a(n)

_____. Positrons are emitted and _____ with electrons in the

nearby tissue. _____ radiation is emitted, which can be detected outside the

body. The amount of radiation detected can match the _____ activity of the

cells in that area, which can be used to determine if the nearby tissue is cancerous.

| X-ray | combine | annihilate | gamma | positron |
| radioactive | | tracer | beta | metabolic |

1 Nuclear radiation has many uses. (Grade 4-6)

a) Draw a line to match the radiation on the left to its common use on the right.

| Gamma radiation | | thickness control for paper |

| Beta radiation | | smoke alarms |

| Alpha radiation | | detecting leaks in underground pipes |

[2]

b) Gamma radiation is also used to sterilise plastic medical equipment instead of boiling it in hot water. Suggest a reason for this.

....

....

[1]

c) PET scans can be used to diagnose cancer.
Explain why some hospitals have their own cyclotron to make positron-emitting isotopes on-site.

....

....

[2]

[Total 5 marks]

2 Sources of radiation can be used in medical imaging to explore internal organs. Technetium-99m is a radioactive isotope that emits gamma radiation. It can be made to bind to calcium. Small calcium deposits appear on damaged heart tissue following a heart attack.

Grade 6-7

a) Explain briefly how technetium-99m could be used to determine if a patient has recently damaged heart tissue.

....

....

....

....

[3]

b) Explain why alpha emitters are not used for medical imaging.

....

....

[2]

[Total 5 marks]

3 Radiotherapy is often used in the treatment of cancer tumours. *Grade 6-7*

a) A patient is receiving cancer treatment. One treatment option is to have a small radiation-emitting implant placed next to their tumour. This implant would then be left inside the body. State the type of radiation the implant would emit. Explain your answer.

....

....

[2]

b) An alternative treatment to the radioactive implant is external radiotherapy. Explain the safety procedures that must be followed. You should make reference to the type of radiation used.

....

....

....

....

....

....

....

....

[5]

[Total 7 marks]

Exam Tip

If you're asked about uses of the different kinds of radiation, think about their properties. Then just apply what you know — if you're trying to detect something from a long way away, then you want something which has a long range.

Section 4 — Radioactivity

Nuclear Fission and Fusion

For the sentences below, state whether they are describing nuclear fission, nuclear fusion or both.

It releases energy. ....

It can start when a nucleus absorbs a neutron. ....

It usually involves large and unstable nuclei. ....

It usually involves light nuclei. ....

Uranium-235 nuclei commonly undergo this. ....

1 Energy can be released from nuclear fusion. (Grade 6-7)

a) State what is meant by nuclear fusion.

....
[1]

b) Which of the following statements about nuclear fusion is correct?

☐ **A** total mass of nuclei before nuclear fusion = total mass of nuclei after nuclear fusion

☐ **B** total mass of nuclei before nuclear fusion > total mass of nuclei after nuclear fusion

☐ **C** total mass of nuclei before nuclear fusion < total mass of nuclei after nuclear fusion

☐ **D** total mass of nuclei before nuclear fusion $\propto$ total mass of nuclei after nuclear fusion
[1]
[Total 2 marks]

2 Fission reactors use chain reactions to produce energy. (Grade 6-7)

a) Describe the steps involved in a chain reaction of nuclei undergoing fission.

....

....

....

....

....

....

....

....
[4]

b) Chain reactions have to be controlled. Explain how a chain reaction is controlled in a nuclear reactor. Your answer should refer to the use of moderators and control rods.

....

....

....

....

....

[4]

[Total 8 marks]

3* Discuss the advantages and disadvantages of using nuclear power to generate electricity. (Grade 6-7)

....

....

....

....

....

....

....

....

....

....

....

....

[Total 6 marks]

4 Explain why experimental fusion reactors currently use more energy than they produce. (Grade 7-9)

....

....

....

....

....

[Total 4 marks]

The Solar System and Gravity

Warm-Up

Complete the diagram below by writing in the names of the planets.
Three have been done for you.

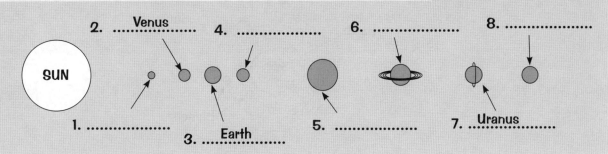

1 Our Solar System contains many different objects.

a) Complete **Figure 1** for each object in the Solar System.

Figure 1

Object	Orbits around	Shape of orbit
Artificial satellites	(Usually) Earth	Approximately circular
Moon	....	....
Comet	....	....

[4]

b) Name **three** other types of object in our Solar System.

....

[3]

c) State the force that keeps these objects in orbit.

....

[1]

[Total 8 marks]

2 Imagine a planet identical to the Earth is discovered in a circular orbit halfway
between the Earth and the Sun. State whether its orbital speed will be faster
than, slower than, or the same as that of the Earth. Explain your answer.

....

....

....

....

....

....

[Total 3 marks]

Changing Ideas about the Universe

1   Over time, ideas about our Solar System have changed. **Figure 1** shows one model of the Solar System.

Figure 1

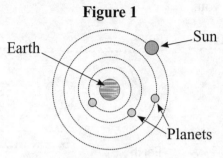

a) State the name of the model shown in **Figure 1**.

    ....
    [1]

b) The model shown in **Figure 1** was replaced by our currently accepted model of the Solar System. Name and briefly describe this currently accepted model.

    ....

    ....

    ....
    [3]

    [Total 4 marks]

2   Theories about the origin of the Universe have changed over time.

a) Which of the following statements is correct for the Steady State model?

    ☐   **A** The density of the Universe is increasing as it expands.

    ☐   **B** The density of the Universe is decreasing as it expands.

    ☐   **C** New matter is constantly being created.

    ☐   **D** There is a finite age for the Universe.
    [1]

b) Another theory that describes the origin of the Universe is the Big Bang theory. Describe briefly the Big Bang theory.

    ....

    ....

    ....
    [3]

c) Name the currently accepted theory for how the Universe began, based on current evidence.

    ....
    [1]

    [Total 5 marks]

Red-shift and CMB Radiation

1 **Figure 1** shows a list of galaxies and their distance from Earth in light years.

Figure 1

Galaxy	Distance From Earth (light years)
Bode's Galaxy	12 million
Southern Pinwheel Galaxy	15 million
Sombrero Galaxy	30 million
Sunflower Galaxy	37 million

The light from all of the galaxies in the table shows red-shift.

a) i) State what is meant by red-shift.

....

....

....

[2]

ii) State which of the galaxies in the table will show the greatest red-shift.
Explain your answer.

....

....

....

....

[3]

iii) Explain how red-shift provides evidence for the Big Bang theory.

....

....

....

....

....

[3]

b) Red-shift can be explained by both the Steady State and Big Bang theories.
Name **one** piece of evidence that only supports the Big Bang model.

....

[1]

[Total 9 marks]

The Life Cycle of Stars

1 **Figure 1** shows the life cycle of a star. (Grade 4-6)

Nebula   Protostar   Main sequence star   X   White dwarf

a) What is the name of the life cycle stage marked X?

☐ **A** red supergiant   ☐ **B** red giant   ☐ **C** red dwarf   ☐ **D** neutron star

[1]

b) State what is meant by a nebula.

....

[1]

c) Name the force responsible for 'pulling together' a nebula to form a protostar.

....

[1]

[Total 3 marks]

2 Our Sun is currently in the main sequence phase of its life cycle. (Grade 6-7)

a) Explain why stars remain a fairly constant size during the main sequence phase.

....

....

....

[3]

b) When the Sun runs out of fuel, it will eject its outer layers to form a planetary nebula, leaving behind a white dwarf, which will gradually cool and fade away. Describe the final life cycle stages of a star with a mass much greater than our Sun, once it has stopped being a red supergiant.

....

....

....

....

....

[3]

[Total 6 marks]

Exam Tip

This is one of those bits of physics where there's just a lot of words and facts you need to learn. You need to remember the names of all of the different stages of the life cycles of stars of different sizes, as well as what's going on in each stage.

Looking into Space

Circle the type of telescope that was responsible for the discovery of CMB radiation.

| Optical telescope | Radio telescope | X-ray telescope |

1 Optical telescopes are used to look at distant objects. **Grade 4-6**

a) High quality optical telescopes have high quality objective lenses and large apertures.
State what is meant by the aperture of a telescope.

....

....

[1]

b) An amateur astronomer wants to improve the images he can see with his optical telescope.
Instead of altering his telescope, he moves it to a location that is higher up and further
away from sources of light. Explain why doing this will improve the images that he sees.

....

....

....

....

....

....

[4]

[Total 5 marks]

2 Astronomers originally used only optical telescopes to view the
Universe. Briefly explain why other telescopes were invented and why
computers are now more commonly used to help observe the Universe. **Grade 6-7**

....

....

....

....

....

....

[Total 4 marks]

Section 6 — Forces and Energy

Energy Transfers and Systems

1   Which of the following is correct for a closed system? *(Grade 4-6)*

☐   **A**   Energy into the system is always larger than energy out of the system.

☐   **B**   Energy out of the system is always larger than energy into the system.

☐   **C**   The net change of energy in a closed system is always zero.

☐   **D**   Closed systems can only be changed by heating.

[Total 1 mark]

2   A filament bulb is connected to a battery, shown in **Figure 1**. You can assume that the wires connecting them have zero resistance. Complete the diagram in **Figure 2** to show the energy transfers that occur when the bulb in connected to the battery. *(Grade 4-6)*

Figure 1   **Figure 2**

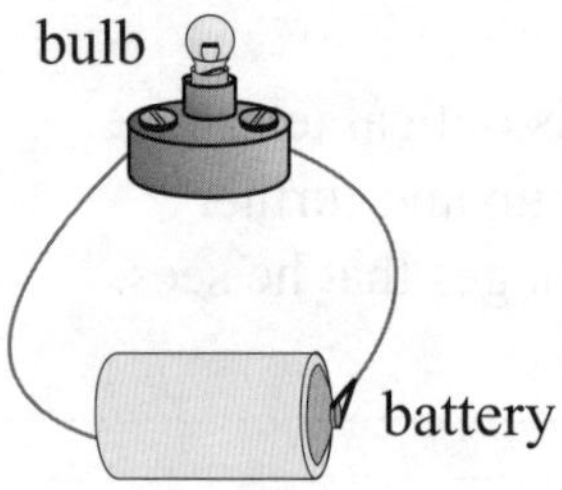

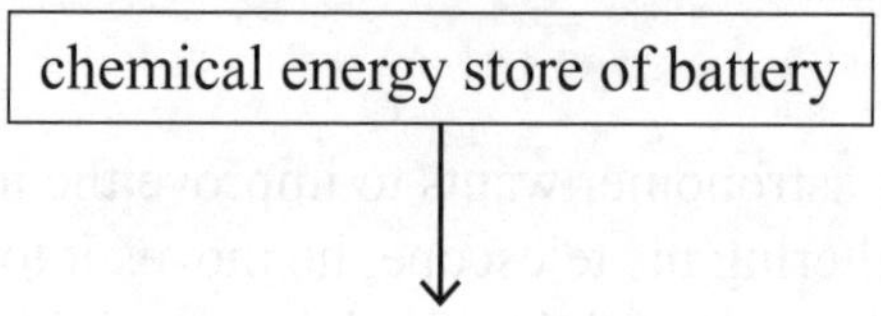

bulb

battery

| chemical energy store of battery |

↓

[Total 3 marks]

3   An 80.0 g apple is a one-object system. The apple is hanging from a branch. *(Grade 6-7)*

a) i) The apple falls from the branch. It reaches a speed of 7.00 m/s just before it hits the ground. Calculate the energy in the apple's kinetic energy store just before it hits the ground.

Energy = ... J

[3]

ii) State what causes the energy transfer within this system.

....

[1]

b) Assuming that there was no air resistance, calculate the height the apple fell from. (Gravitational field strength = 10 N/kg.)

Height = ... m

[4]

[Total 7 marks]

Work Done and Power

Complete the sentences below using the words or phrases from the box.
You can only use each option once and you do not need to use every option.

As a rubber ball falls, it experiences a .... due to ....·

.... is done on the ball and .... is transferred from the ball's

.... energy store to its .... energy store.

| force | work | chemical potential | | kinetic | gravity |
| elastic potential | energy | | gravitational potential | heating | |

1   Which of these is the definition of power?   (Grade 4-6)

  ☐   **A** Power is the total work done by an object.

  ☐   **B** Power is the rate of energy transfer.

  ☐   **C** Power is the total energy transferred to an object.

  ☐   **D** Power is the minimum work done to an object to cause it to move.

[Total 1 mark]

2   A student is investigating the work done by different washing machines during a standard washing cycle. **Figure 1** shows the manufacturer's data about three machines.   (Grade 6-7)

Figure 1

Machine	Power	Time needed
A	600 W	125 minutes
B	400 W	160 minutes
C	....	125 minutes

a)   Calculate the work done by machine A during its standard washing cycle.
Give your answer in kJ.

Work done = ... kJ

[4]

b)   Machine C's standard cycle lasts for 125 minutes. It does 3 930 000 J of work in that time.
Complete the table in **Figure 1** by calculating the power of machine C.

[2]

[Total 6 marks]

3 A woman pushes a 20 kg wheelbarrow 15 m along a flat path using a horizontal force of 50 N. *Grade 6-7*

a) i) State the equation that links work done, force applied and distance moved in the direction of the force.

....
[1]

ii) Calculate the work done by the woman.

Work done = ... J
[2]

b) Work has to be done against the frictional forces acting on the wheel of the wheelbarrow. Explain the effect this has on the temperature of the wheel.

....

....

....
[2]

[Total 5 marks]

4 A mechanic replaces a worn out engine of a car with a new, more efficient one. The old engine had a useful output power of 52 kW and an efficiency of 25%. The new engine has an efficiency of 30%. *Grade 7-9*

a) Calculate the useful output power of the new engine. You can assume that the input power of both engines is the same.

Output power = ... W
[5]

b) Explain the effect replacing the engine will have on the time taken for the car to accelerate from rest to 20 m/s.

....

....

....

....
[3]

[Total 8 marks]

Target AO3

5   A student wants to measure the useful power output of a motor.

The student has the following equipment she can use in an experiment:
- a motor, attached to an axle
- a power supply and basic circuitry
- a length of string
- a clamp and clamp stand
- a metre ruler
- a stopwatch
- a 1 kg mass

a)* Describe an experiment that the student could perform to determine
the useful power output of the motor, using the equipment listed.
You should include explanation of how the student can ensure the results are valid.

....

....

....

....

....

....

....

....

....

....

....
                                                                                                          [6]

b) **Figure 2** shows the display of the stopwatch when the
student takes a time measurement during her experiment.
The time recorded was 18.5 s.

Figure 2

i) State the smallest increment of time the stopwatch can measure.

....
                                                                        [1]

ii) Suggest why any errors in the student's time measurements are likely
to be larger than the smallest increment of time that can be measured by the stopwatch.

....

....
                                                                                                          [2]
                                                                               [Total 9 marks]

Exam Tip

Question 5a) is an example of a question which tests how well you can <u>write</u> (as well as your scientific knowledge).
These questions tend to be worth more marks than the other exam questions, so it's worth learning how to answer them
properly. Try to plan how you'll structure your answer first before you start, so you make sure you cover all the key points.

Section 6 — Forces and Energy

76

Forces

1 Forces are caused by interactions between objects. `Grade 4-6`

   a) Forces can be split into contact and non-contact forces.

     i) Describe what is meant by a 'contact force'.

     ....

     ....

                                                                             [1]

     ii) Give **two** examples of a contact force.

       1. ....

       2. ....

                                                                            [2]

   b) Give **one** example of a non-contact force.

   ....

                                                                            [1]

                                  [Total 4 marks]

2 **Figure 1** shows four runners who are running in windy weather. Which runner is experiencing the largest horizontal resultant force? `Grade 4-6`

Figure 1

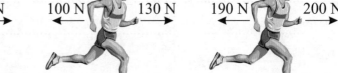

80 N ← → 100 N   10 N ← → 5 N   100 N ← → 130 N   190 N ← → 200 N

    A ☐   B ☐   C ☐   D ☐

                                    [Total 1 mark]

3 **Figure 2** shows a toy car. The weight of the car is 20 N. As it accelerates, it experiences a driving force of 30 N. There is a 5 N resistive force acting against the motion of the car. Add arrows to **Figure 2** to create a free body force diagram for the car. `Grade 6-7`

Figure 2

                                    [Total 2 marks]

Section 6 — Forces and Energy

4   **Figure 3** shows an incomplete diagram of the forces acting on a
     ladder leaning against a wall. There is no friction between the ladder
     and the wall but there is friction between the ladder and the ground.

Figure 3

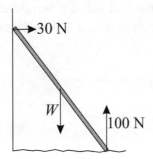

a) Complete **Figure 3** by drawing the missing frictional force.

[2]

b) Using **Figure 3**, determine the weight of the ladder, W.

Weight = ... N

[1]

[Total 3 marks]

5   **Figure 4** shows a pair of identical magnets. There is a force of repulsion between them.

Figure 4

Magnet A   Magnet B

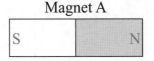   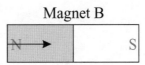

a) The arrow in **Figure 4** shows the force exerted on magnet B by magnet A. Complete the diagram
    in **Figure 4** by drawing another arrow representing the force that magnet B exerts on magnet A.

[2]

b) Explain what is causing the force between the two magnets.

....

....

[1]

c) Magnet B is replaced by a much stronger magnet.
    The strength of magnet A and the orientation of the magnets remains the same.
    Describe how you would redraw the arrows on the diagram to show this new force interaction.

....

....

[2]

[Total 5 marks]

Exam Tip

Make sure you get your head around the difference between an interaction pair and a free body force diagram.
Free body force diagrams show the forces acting on a single object, whereas interaction pairs act on different objects.

Forces and Vector Diagrams

Warm-Up

Find the sizes of the horizontal and vertical components of the force shown on the right. Each side of a square represents 1 N.

Horizontal component = ... N

Vertical component = ... N

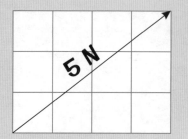

1   **Figure 1** shows a girl on a swing. Her weight of 500 N acts vertically downwards and a tension force of 250 N acts on the ropes at an angle of 30° to the horizontal.

Figure 1

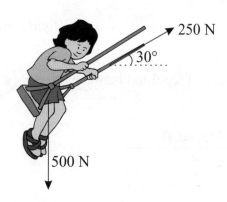

250 N

30°

500 N

Figure 2

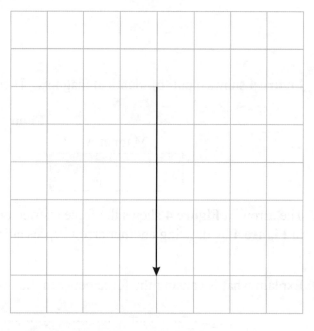

a)   **Figure 2** shows an incomplete scale drawing for the forces acting on the girl.
Only the girl's weight has been drawn so far. Calculate the scale used in the drawing.

.... cm = ... N
[1]

b)   Complete the scale drawing in **Figure 2** to find the magnitude of the resultant force acting on the girl.

Magnitude = ... N
[2]

[Total 3 marks]

2 One of the events at a school sports day is a three-way tug of war.
Three teams each pull on a rope, all three of which are attached to a metal ring. **Figure 3** shows the forces exerted on the ring. It is not drawn to scale.

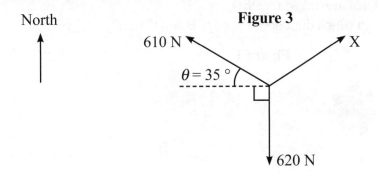

North

Figure 3

610 N

X

$\theta = 35°$

620 N

The ring is in equilibrium and does not move. Use the grid in **Figure 4** to create a scale drawing to determine the magnitude and direction as a bearing of force X.

Figure 4

Magnitude of force X = ... N

Direction = ... °

[Total 5 marks]

Section 6 — Forces and Energy

Moments

1   **Figure 1** shows several cogs that are linked together.
    If cog A is turned clockwise, in which direction will cogs B and C turn?

Figure 1

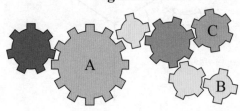

Cog B: ....   Cog C: ....

[Total 2 marks]

2   A mechanic creates a moment by applying a force of 50 N perpendicular to the end
    of a spanner. The distance between the pivot and the end of the spanner is 12 cm.

a) State what is meant by a moment.

    ....
    [1]

b) Calculate the moment created by the mechanic. Give the unit. Use the equation:
    moment of a force = force × distance normal to the direction of the force.

                                    Moment = ... Unit = ...
    [3]

    [Total 4 marks]

3   Two children are playing outside. One child, with a weight of 420 N,
    stands on one end of a plank of wood as shown in **Figure 2**.
    The other child pushes down on the opposite end of the plank of wood.

Figure 2

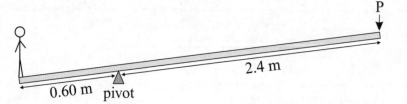

Calculate the force the child need to apply to point P in order to lift the child stood on the plank.

                                    Force = ... N
    [Total 3 marks]

4 **Figure 3** shows three gears linked together.

For one complete turn of A, calculate
how many times cogs B and C turn.

Figure 3

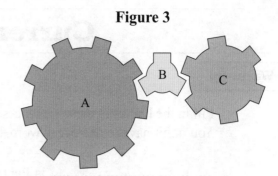

Cog B = ... turns

Cog C = ... turns

[Total 3 marks]

5 A student is investigating the principle of moments. **Figure 4** shows the equipment used. The beam has a mass of 20 N. The fulcrum is placed a distance, x, from the centre of mass of the beam. The centre of mass is the point at which the weight of the beam acts. Masses are added to either side of the beam. The masses and their distance from the fulcrum required to balance the beam are recorded.

Figure 4

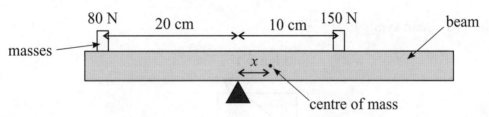

a) Give **one** control variable for the experiment shown in **Figure 4**.

....

[1]

b) The student repeats the experiment on another day, using identical equipment. However, he uses a different mass balance to find the mass of each unit mass. He finds that all of his mass readings have increased by 0.5 g. State the type of error this would have caused in his experiment.

....

[1]

c) The beam in **Figure 4** is balanced.
Calculate the distance between the fulcrum and the centre of mass of the beam.

x = ... cm

[5]

[Total 7 marks]

Exam Tip

Take longer moment questions step-by-step — it might even help to label each force (e.g. A, B) so you can keep track of them. Work out the moment caused by each force before you try to work out the overall moment acting on an object.

Section 6 — Forces and Energy

Current and Circuits

Fill in the blanks in these sentences with the words below.
You don't have to use every word, but each word can only be used once.

.... is the rate of flow of electric charge (electrons) around a circuit.

A current will flow around a circuit if the circuit is .... and there is a

source of ....

The current flowing through a component .... when the potential difference

across it increases or when the resistance of the component ....

coulomb		energy	current	increases
potential difference	decreases	closed	

1   **Figure 1** shows a circuit symbol.

Figure 1

The circuit symbol shown is a

☐   **A**   resistor.

☐   **B**   variable resistor.

☐   **C**   thermistor.

☐   **D**   fuse.

[Total 1 mark]

 2   A current of 3.5 A flows through a simple circuit containing a battery and a resistor.

a)   Calculate how much charge passes through the light bulb in 120 seconds.

Charge = ... C

[3]

b)   Calculate how long it will take for 770 C to pass through the light bulb.

Time = ... s

[3]

[Total 6 marks]

Potential Difference and Resistance

1   A kettle needs 276 000 J of energy to be electrically transferred to it in order to bring water to the boil. It is connected to the mains supply which has a voltage of 230 V.

   a) Calculate the amount of charge that passes through the kettle to bring the water to the boil.

Charge = ... C

[3]

   b) A toaster is connected to the same mains supply. When a slice of bread is toasted, the charge that passes through the toaster is 1000 C.

Calculate the energy transferred to toast the slice of bread. Give your answer in kJ.

Energy transferred = ... kJ

[2]

[Total 5 marks]

 2   When a potential difference of 18 V is applied across a resistor, a current of 3 A flows through it.

   a) Calculate the resistance of the resistor. State the units of your answer.

Resistance = ... Units ....

[4]

   b) Over time, the current through the resistor begins to decrease. Explain why this happens.

....

....

....

....

....

[4]

[Total 8 marks]

Investigating Components

1 Voltmeters and ammeters are used to investigate circuits. (Grade 4-6)

a) A voltmeter should always be connected

☐ **A** in series with the component.

☐ **B** in series with the source of potential difference.

☐ **C** in parallel with a resistor.

☐ **D** in parallel with the component.

[1]

b) **Figure 1** shows a circuit. Draw an ammeter in an appropriate place on the diagram to measure the current flowing through the bulb.

Figure 1

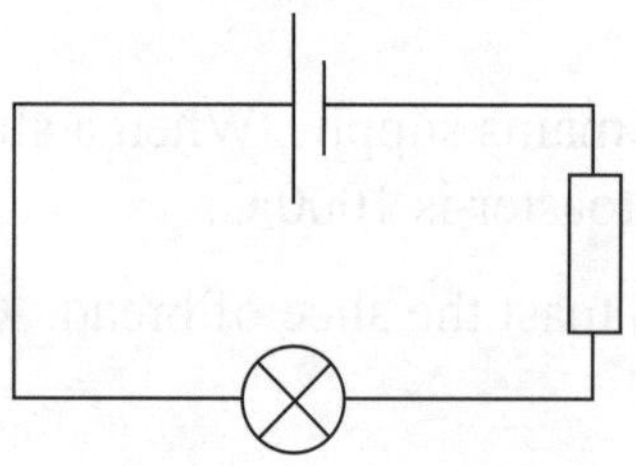

[1]
[Total 2 marks]

PRACTICAL

2 A student used the circuit in **Figure 2** to find the *I-V* characteristic of a filament lamp. (Grade 4-6)

a) Explain the purpose of the variable d.c. source in the circuit.

Figure 2

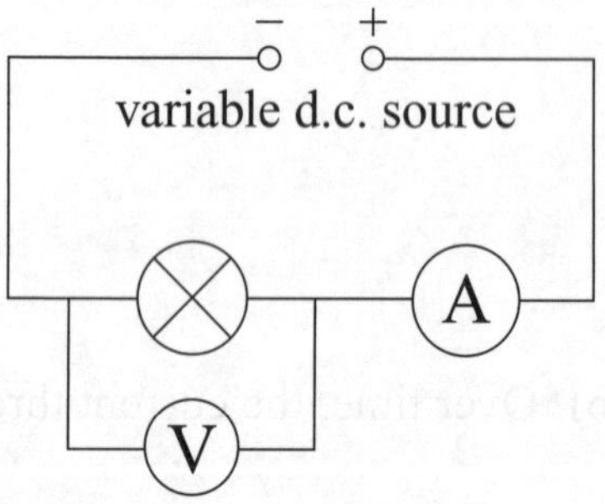

....

....

....

....

[2]

b) The student's method involves disconnecting the variable d.c. source every 2 minutes for 30 seconds. Explain how this will improve the student's results.

....

....

[2]
[Total 4 marks]

Target AO3

3   A student creates a test circuit containing a diode, as shown in **Figure 3**.

Grade
6-7

Figure 3

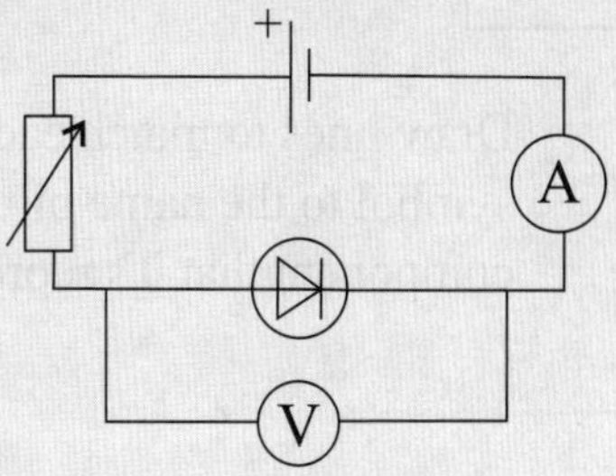

a) Describe a method the student could use to investigate how the resistance of the diode changes with current.

....

....

....

....

....

....

....

....

[3]

The student carries out the experiment and plots her results on a graph, shown in **Figure 4**.

Figure 4

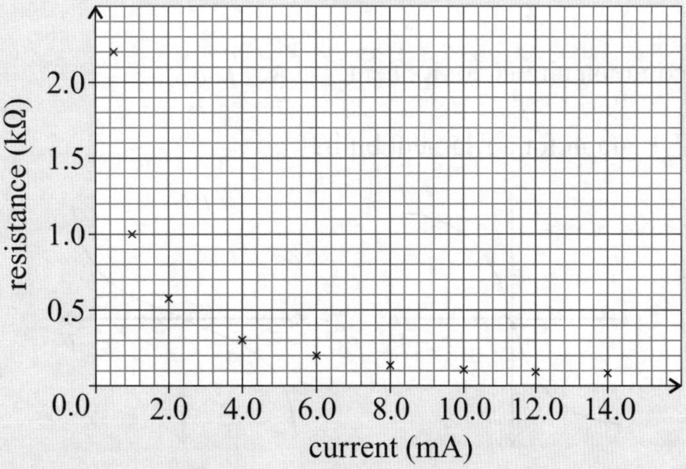

b) Draw a curve of best fit on **Figure 4**.

[1]

c) The student states, "From my results, I can conclude that the greater the magnitude of the current through the diode, the lower the resistance." Explain why the student cannot make this conclusion from her results.

....

....

....

....

[2]

[Total 6 marks]

Section 7 — Electricity and Circuits

Circuit Devices

Draw lines to match each circuit symbol to the name of the component that it's representing.

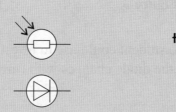

thermistor

LDR

diode

1 The resistance of a thermistor changes depending on its surroundings. Grade 4-6

a) State what happens to the resistance of a thermistor as the surrounding temperature increases.

....

[1]

b) Give **one** example of a device that uses a thermistor.

....

[1]

[Total 2 marks]

2 Filament bulbs are a common circuit component. Grade 6-7

a) Which is the correct *I-V* graph for a filament bulb?

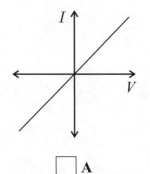 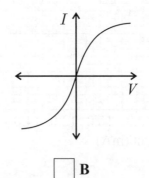 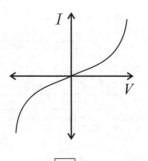 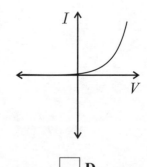

☐ **A**   ☐ **B**   ☐ **C**   ☐ **D**

[1]

b) Explain why the *I-V* graph for a filament bulb has this shape.

....

....

....

[2]

[Total 3 marks]

Series and Parallel Circuits

1   **Figure 1** shows a number of circuits. Tick the box below the diagram that shows all the components connected in series.

Figure 1

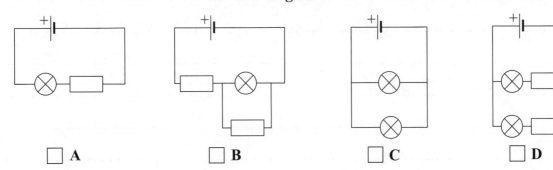

☐ **A**   ☐ **B**   ☐ **C**   ☐ **D**

[Total 1 mark]

2   Draw a circuit diagram consisting of a cell and two LDRs connected in parallel.

[Total 2 marks]

3   In the circuit in **Figure 2**, the reading on the ammeter is 75 mA.

a) Calculate the total resistance of the two resistors.   **Figure 2**

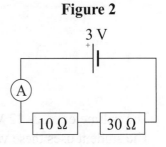

Resistance = ... Ω

[1]

b) Calculate the potential difference across the 30 Ω resistor.

Potential Difference = ... V

[3]

[Total 4 marks]

88

4* Explain why adding resistors in series with each other increases the total resistance of the resistors, whilst adding resistors in parallel with each other decreases the total resistance of the resistors.

....

....

....

....

....

....

....

....

....

....

....

....

[Total 6 marks]

PRACTICAL

5 A student is investigating series and parallel circuits, using bulbs which are labelled as having the same resistance. She sets up the circuit shown in **Figure 3**.

Figure 3

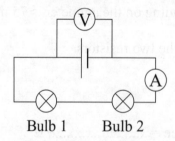

Bulb 1   Bulb 2

The voltmeter reads 12 V and the ammeter reads 0.25 A.
The student uses these values to calculate the resistance of each bulb.

a) Calculate the resistance of each bulb, assuming that the bulbs do have the same resistance.

Resistance = ... Ω

[3]

Section 7 — Electricity and Circuits

b) The student then adds a third bulb to the circuit, as shown in **Figure 4**.

Figure 4

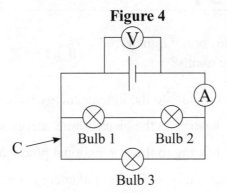

i) Assuming that bulb 3 is identical to bulbs 1 and 2, find the new current through the ammeter.

Current = ... A

[2]

ii) The student observes that bulb 3 is brighter than bulbs 1 and 2. Explain why.

....

....

[2]

c) The student then adds a resistor to the circuit in **Figure 4**, at the point marked C.

i) Describe the effect of this on the current through the ammeter.

....

[1]

ii) State how this affects the brightness of the three bulbs.

....

....

[2]

d) When the student's teacher marks her experiment, he says she should have measured the potential difference across and the current through each bulb throughout the experiment. Give **two** reasons why.

....

....

....

[2]

[Total 12 marks]

Exam Tip

Although we talk about series and parallel circuits as separate things, real circuits are often a mix — you might get a question where some components are connected in series with each other, but where there's more than one branch to the circuit. Don't panic, just remember that the rules of parallel circuits apply when you're looking at the different branches, and the rules of series circuits apply when you're looking at the components connected along one branch.

Energy in Circuits

1 Which of the following describes the energy transferred to an electric heater connected to the mains?

Grade 4-6

☐ **A**   Energy is transferred electrically to the kinetic energy store of the heater.

☐ **B**   Energy is transferred by heating to the electrostatic energy store of the heater.

☐ **C**   Energy is transferred by heating to the gravitational potential energy store of the heater.

☐ **D**   Energy is transferred electrically to the thermal energy store of the heater.

[Total 1 mark]

2 A hairdryer contains of a motor which turns a fan and a heating element.

Grade 6-7

a) State **one** part of the hairdryer where the heating effect of a current is **useful**.

....

[1]

b) State **one** part of the hairdryer where the heating effect of a current is **not useful**.

....

[1]

c) The hairdryer becomes less efficient the longer it is left on for. Explain why.

....

....

....

[3]

[Total 5 marks]

3 A kettle is filled with a litre of water from the cold tap.

Grade 6-7

a) It takes 355 000 J of energy to bring a litre of water to the boil. The kettle is attached to the mains, at 230 V, and the current through the kettle is 12 A. Calculate how long it should take the kettle to boil, to the nearest second.

Time = ... s

[3]

b) State **one** assumption that you made in order to answer part a).

....

....

[1]

[Total 4 marks]

Power in Circuits

1   A child is playing with a toy car. The car is powered by a battery and has two speed settings — fast and slow.

a) The child sets the speed to slow and drives the car for 20 seconds. The power of the car at this speed is 50 W. Calculate the energy transferred by the car.

Energy transferred = ... J

[3]

b) The child now sets the speed to fast. The power of the car at this speed is 75 W. Explain why the battery runs down more quickly when the car is set at a higher speed.

....

....

[2]

[Total 5 marks]

2   Fans use a motor to turn a set of blades.

a) A 75 W ceiling fan in an office is powered by the mains supply at 230 V. Calculate the current supplied to the fan.

Current = ... A

[3]

b) A smaller fan on someone's desk runs from a computer's USB port. It has a power of 2.5 W, and draws a current of 0.50 A. Calculate its resistance.

Resistance = ... Ω

[3]

The ceiling fan from part a) breaks and the company investigate replacing it with a standing fan. They look at three models, A-C, summarised in **Figure 1**.

Figure 1

Model	Power rating / W	Customer reviews
A	50	very noisy
B	40	breaks frequently, a bit small
C	45	quiet and reliable

c) i) Give the model that transfers energy at the fastest rate.   ....

[1]

ii) Explain why your answer to part c) i) may not be the most efficient fan for cooling the office.

....

....

[2]

[Total 9 marks]

Section 7 — Electricity and Circuits

Electricity in the Home

Warm-Up

In the table below, put a tick next to each statement to show whether it applies to direct current or alternating current.

	Direct current	Alternating current
Describes the current supplied by a battery		
Produced by a voltage that constantly changes direction		
Describes the current supplied by the UK mains		
Produced by a voltage with a constant direction		

1 Most houses in the UK are connected to the mains supply. (Grade 4-6)

a) State the potential difference and frequency of the UK mains electricity supply.

....

[1]

b) A kettle is plugged into the mains with a three-core cable containing a live wire, a neutral wire and an earth wire.

i) State the colours of the live, neutral, and earth wires.

Live: ....

Neutral: ....

Earth: ....

[2]

ii) Complete the table in **Figure 1** to show the sizes of the potential differences between the wires that make up the three-core cable.

Figure 1

Wires	Potential difference / V
Live wire and neutral wire	....
Neutral wire and earth wire	....
Earth wire and live wire	....

[3]

[Total 6 marks]

2 A radio develops a fault such that the live wire is in electrical contact with the neutral wire. (Grade 6-7)

Explain whether you think the radio will work while this fault remains.

....

....

....

....

[Total 3 marks]

3 The cable that connects an iron to the mains supply has become worn with use. There is no insulation covering part of the live wire. The iron is plugged in, but switched off. (Grade 6-7) ✗

a) State **two** purposes of the insulation that covers the live wire.

....

....

....

[2]

b) A man switches on the iron and touches the exposed live wire. He receives an electric shock. Explain why he receives an electric shock. You should refer to the electrical potential of the man in your answer.

....

....

....

....

[3]

c) The socket is switched off and the iron is unplugged.
Explain whether there is still a danger of the man receiving an electric shock from the plug socket.

....

....

....

....

[3]

[Total 8 marks]

Exam Tip

The voltage-time graph for an alternating current has a similar shape to the wave shown on p.29. The frequency of an alternating current is how many cycles it completes per second, where one cycle is, for example, from one crest to the next crest (or from one trough to the next trough). It's measured in Hz, just like wave frequency.

Section 7 — Electricity and Circuits

Fuses and Earthing

1 **Figure 1** shows an old-fashioned household fuse box.

Figure 1

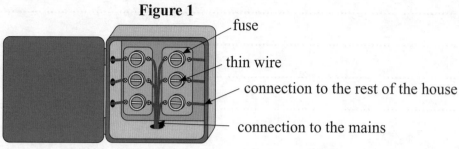

fuse

thin wire

connection to the rest of the house

connection to the mains

a) Explain why houses have fuse boxes.

....

[1]

b) In old-fashioned fuse boxes like this, home-owners sometimes replaced old fuses with pennies.
Explain why replacing fuses with pennies like this was dangerous.

....

....

[1]

c) Most modern houses uses circuit breakers, rather than fuse boxes.
Give **one** advantage and **one** disadvantage of using circuit breakers instead of fuses.

Advantage: ....

Disadvantage: ....

[2]

[Total 4 marks]

2 Many electrical devices include an Earth wire.

a) Explain how the earth wire and fuse work when a fault develops with a metal appliance.

....

....

....

....

[3]

b) The fuse in an electric heater is rated at 13 A. The fuse in a clock radio is rated at 3 A.
Suggest why these devices need fuses with different ratings.

....

....

....

[2]

[Total 6 marks]

Static Electricity

1 A plastic acetate rod is rubbed with a cloth. A positive static charge builds up on the rod. **Grade 6-7**

a) Explain how a static charge builds up on the rod.

....

....

....

[2]

b) i) A student holds the rod close to some small scraps of paper.
The scraps move up towards the rod. Explain why this occurs.

....

....

....

....

....

[3]

ii) The student then tries the same experiment with a metal rod, but the paper doesn't move.
Explain why the experiment doesn't work with a metal rod.

....

....

....

[3]

[Total 8 marks]

2 A man walks up some carpeted stairs. The handrail is made of metal and is electrically connected to earth. When he puts his hand near the rail, there is a spark. **Grade 7-9**

a) The carpet and the man's shoes rub together, making the man electrically charged.
Explain why there is a spark between the man's hand and the rail.

....

....

[2]

b) The spark leapt from the man to the handrail.
State and explain whether the man was positively or negatively charged.

....

....

....

[3]

[Total 5 marks]

Uses and Dangers of Static Electricity

Use the phrases in the box to fill in the gaps in the sentences below. Not all of the phrases in the box are used in the sentences. Some phrases may be used more than once.

Electrostatic sprayers work by electrically charging droplets of paint. The charge on each

drop is _____ the charge on the other drops, so they _____

each other. This means you get a very fine spray. The charge on the object being painted

is _____ the charge of the paint droplets, so it _____ them.

| the same as | opposite to | repel | attract | repels | attracts |

1 **Figure 1** shows a lightning bolt during a storm. Lightning is caused by a large build up of static electricity.

Grade 6-7

Figure 1

Describe briefly how static electricity builds up in a storm cloud and results in lightning.

....

....

....

....

[Total 3 marks]

2 Fuel tankers are used to refill large underground tanks of petrol at petrol stations. The tanker drivers have to be very cautious of static electricity when refilling the fuel tanks.

Grade 6-7

a) Explain why static electricity is dangerous when filling up petrol tanks.

....

....

....

[2]

b) State and explain **one** way of reducing this danger.

....

....

....

[2]

[Total 4 marks]

Electric Fields

1   All electrically charged objects produce an electric field.   (Grade 4-6)

a)   An electric field is

☐   **A**   a region where a negative charge will always experience a repulsive force.

☐   **B**   a region where an electric charge experiences a force.

☐   **C**   a region where an electric charge experiences no force.

☐   **D**   a region where a negative charge will always experience an attractive force.

[1]

b)   **Figure 1** shows a pair of parallel, charged plates. There is a uniform field between the plates.
     Draw the electric field lines for these plates.

Figure 1

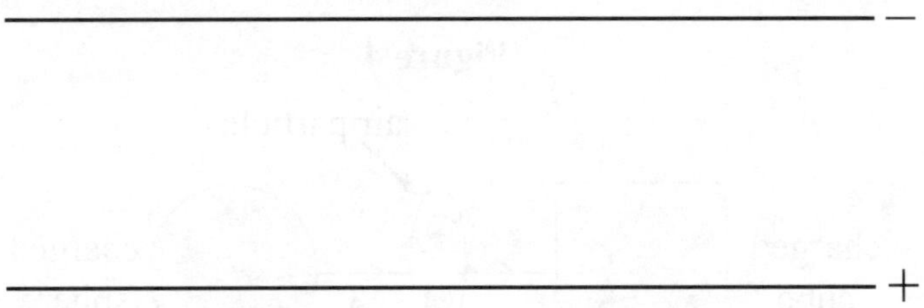

—————————————————————————   −

—————————————————————————   +

[2]

c)   i)   Two charged spheres are placed near each other. **Figure 2** shows some of their field lines.
          Label the diagram to show the type of charge (positive or negative) on each sphere.

Figure 2

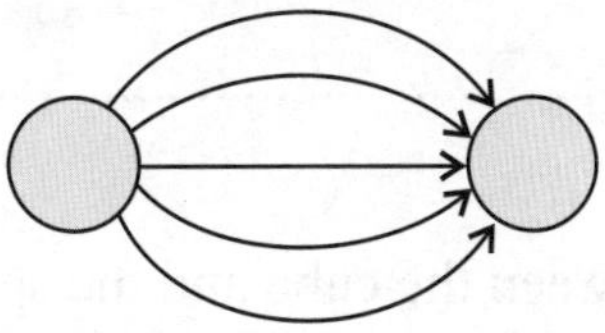

[1]

   ii)   Describe what would happen to the charges if they were free to move.

   ....

[1]

d)   i)   **Figure 3** shows an isolated point charge. Draw the electric field lines for this charge.

Figure 3

⊖

[3]

ii) State what happens to the strength of the field as you move away from the point charge in **Figure 3**.

....

[1]

iii) Describe how the field lines drawn in **Figure 3** would differ if the charge in **Figure 3** was a positive point charge of the same magnitude.

....

....

[1]

[Total 10 marks]

2   **Figure 4** shows an electric field between two charged objects that are fixed in place. An air particle is also shown (not to scale). The air particle is made up of a positively charged nucleus and negatively charged electrons. It experiences a non-contact force.

Figure 4

air particle

charged cube

charged sphere

electric field

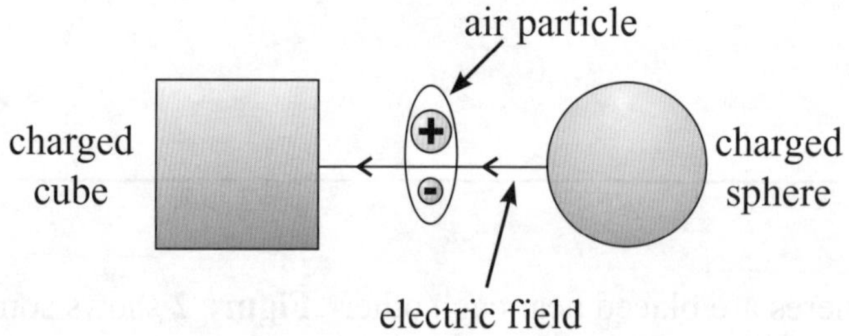

a) The potential difference between the cube and the sphere is increased. State what happens to the size of the force experienced by the air particle.

....

[1]

b) When the potential difference between the cube and the sphere is high enough, the air particle breaks apart and it becomes ionised. Explain why this happens.

....

....

....

....

[3]

c) Describe what happens once the air particles between the cube and sphere have become ionised.

....

....

[2]

[Total 6 marks]

Exam Tip

Make sure you include arrows on any field lines you draw — they tell you which direction the electric field is acting in.

Section 8 — Electric and Magnetic Fields

Magnets and Magnetic Fields

For each statement, circle whether it is true (T) or false (F).

A magnetic field is a region where other magnets experience a force.   T / F

Field lines show the direction a force would act on a south pole at that point in the field.   T / F

The further away from a magnet you get, the weaker the field is.   T / F

1   All magnets produce magnetic fields.   (Grade 4-6)

a) Which of the following statements is correct for magnets?

☐   **A**   Like poles attract each other.

☐   **B**   Magnetic fields are weakest at the poles of a magnet.

☐   **C**   Unlike poles attract each other.

☐   **D**   Magnetic field lines go from the south pole to the north pole.   *[1]*

b) **Figure 1** shows a bar magnet. Draw the magnetic field lines onto the diagram in **Figure 1**.

Figure 1

| N   S |

[3]

Two bar magnets are placed near to each other, as shown in **Figure 2**.

Figure 2

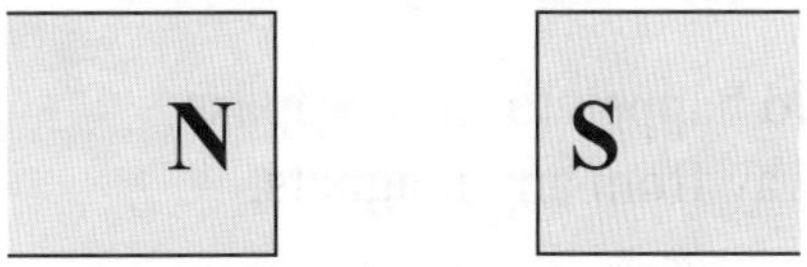

| N | | S |

c) i) A uniform magnetic field is created between them. Explain what is meant by a uniform field.

....

....   *[1]*

ii) Draw the uniform field between the two poles shown in **Figure 2**.

[2]

[Total 7 marks]

2 A student places two magnetic objects near to each other on a flat, frictionless surface. **Figure 3** shows their magnetic fields. The student then releases the objects at the same time.

Grade 6-7

Figure 3

State and explain the behaviour of the two objects once they are released.

....

....

....

[Total 3 marks]

3 A student wants to investigate the magnetic field of a horseshoe magnet, shown in **Figure 4**.

Grade 6-7

Figure 4

a) Describe how a compass could be used to determine the magnetic field pattern of the magnet.

....

....

....

....

....

....

....

....

....

....

....

....

[4]

b) State and explain what would happen to the compass if you were to move it far away from any magnets.

....

....

....

[2]

[Total 6 marks]

Exam Tip

Iron filings can also be used to see the shape of a magnetic field — but remember, they won't show you its direction.

Section 8 — Electric and Magnetic Fields

Permanent and Induced Magnets

1   Magnets can be permanent or induced.   *Grade 4-6*

a) Describe the difference between a permanent magnet and an induced magnet.

....

....

....

[2]

b) Name **two** magnetic materials.

1. ....

2. ....

[2]

c) State **one** everyday use of magnets.

....

[1]

[Total 5 marks]

2   A block of cobalt is held in place near to a bar magnet, as shown in **Figure 1**.   *Grade 6-7*

Figure 1

N	S		•P
bar magnet		cobalt	

a) A steel paperclip is placed against the block of cobalt at point P, shown on **Figure 1**.
The paperclip sticks to the block of cobalt. Explain why this happens.

....

....

....

....

....

....

[3]

b) The bar magnet is removed. Explain what happens to the paperclip.

....

....

....

[2]

[Total 5 marks]

Electromagnetism and the Motor Effect

Warm-Up

The diagram shows a left hand being used for Fleming's left hand rule.
Using **three** of the labels below, label the thumb and fingers in the diagram.

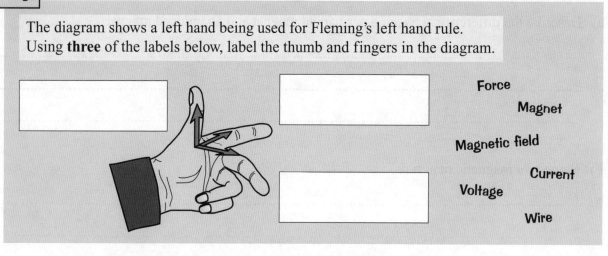

Force

Magnet

Magnetic field

Current

Voltage

Wire

1   A wire is placed between two magnets, as shown in **Figure 1**.
A current is flowing through the wire, in the direction shown.

Grade 4-6

Figure 1

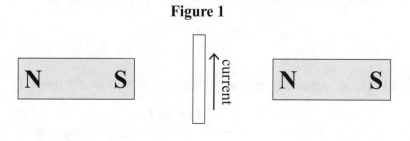

current

a) What will happen to the wire?

☐ **A** It will move to the left.

☐ **B** It will move away from you, into the paper.

☐ **C** It will move towards you, out of the paper.

☐ **D** It will remain stationary.

[1]

b) This effect is called the motor effect. Explain the cause of the motor effect.

....

....

[2]

c) State **three** factors which determine the magnitude of the force acting on the wire.

1. ....

2. ....

3. ....

[3]

[Total 6 marks]

2   **Figure 2** shows a wire which has a current flowing through it.
The arrow shows the direction of the current.

Figure 2

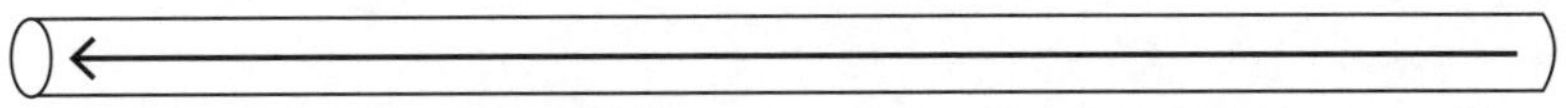

a) The flow of charge creates a magnetic field around the wire.
Draw field lines on **Figure 2** showing the direction of the magnetic field created.

[2]

b) The direction of the current is reversed. State the effect this will have on the magnetic field.

....

....

[1]

c) Give **one** way to increase the strength of the magnetic field produced by the wire.

....

[1]

[Total 4 marks]

3   A 0.75 m section of wire, carrying a current of 0.4 A, is placed into a magnetic field, shown
in **Figure 3**. When the wire is perpendicular to the field, it experiences a force of 1.2 N.

Figure 3

wire

| S | • | N |

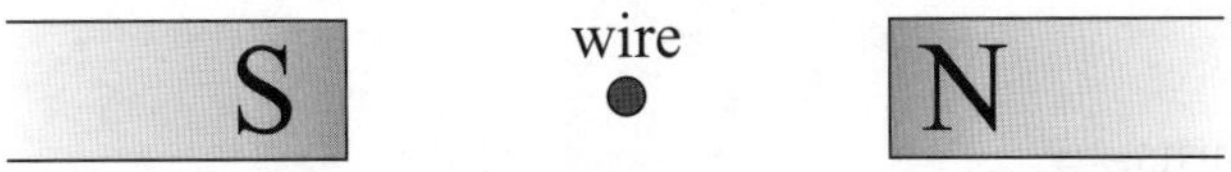

Calculate the magnetic flux density of the field. Give the correct unit in your answer.

Magnetic flux density = ...

Unit = ...

[Total 4 marks]

Exam Tip

Don't get confused between which hand you're using for a situation. Use your right hand for finding the magnetic field
produced by a current-carrying conductor and your left hand for the force acting on a wire in a magnetic field.

Section 8 — Electric and Magnetic Fields

Motors and Solenoids

1 Solenoids are an example of an electromagnet. (Grade 4-6)

a) State what is meant by an electromagnet.

....

....

[1]

b) i) Describe the magnetic field inside the centre of a solenoid.

....

....

[2]

ii) Describe the magnetic field of a solenoid outside of the solenoid.

....

....

[2]

[Total 5 marks]

2 **Figure 1** shows part of a basic d.c. motor. A coil of wire is positioned between two magnetic poles and allowed to rotate. (Grade 6-7)

Figure 1

N   S
−
+

a) Explain why the coil turns.

....

....

....

[2]

b) Explain how a direct current can be used to make the coil in **Figure 1** continue to rotate in the same direction.

....

....

....

....

[2]

[Total 4 marks]

Electromagnetic Induction in Transformers

Warm-Up

For each option, circle the word that correctly completes each sentence.

Transformers consist of two coils of wire, wrapped around a(n) (plastic / iron) core.

Transformers can change the size of (alternating / direct) potential differences.

(Step-up / Step-down) transformers decrease the output potential difference.

(Step-up / Step-down) transformers decrease the output current.

1   This question is about statements 1 and 2, shown below.

Statement 1: A potential difference is induced when an electrical
conductor moves relative to a magnetic field.

Statement 2: A potential difference is induced when there is a change in
the magnetic field around an electrical conductor.

Which of the following is correct?

☐ **A** Only statement 1 is true.   ☐ **C** Both statements 1 and 2 are true.

☐ **B** Only statement 2 is true.   ☐ **D** Neither statement 1 nor 2 is true.

[Total 1 mark]

2   A transformer is 100% efficient. The current through the primary coil is 20.0 A
and the potential difference across it is 30.0 V. The potential difference across
the secondary coil is 40.0 V. Calculate the current through the secondary coil.

Current = ... A
[Total 3 marks]

3   A student sets up a simple circuit to measure the current generated when he moves
a magnet in and out of a coil. The set-up of his apparatus is shown in **Figure 1**.

Figure 1

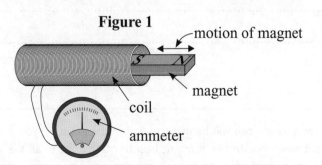

a) State and explain whether the set-up in **Figure 1** generates alternating or direct current.

....

....

....

....

[3]

b) State **three** ways to increase the potential difference induced by the set-up in **Figure 1**.

1. ....

2. ....

3. ....

[3]

[Total 6 marks]

4   Transformers use electromagnetic induction to increase or decrease the potential difference that is supplied to them.   (Grade 7-9)

a)* Explain how a step-up transformer uses electromagnetic induction to increase its output potential difference. Your answer should refer to the number of turns on each coil of the transformer.

....

....

....

....

....

....

....

....

....

....

[6]

b) The current generated in the secondary coil of the transformer creates its own magnetic field. Describe the direction of this magnetic field in relation to the magnetic field that caused it.

....

....

[1]

[Total 7 marks]

Exam Tip

The equation you need for question two will be given to you in the exam — you just have to choose the correct equation from the list. To work out which one to use, it might help to make a list of all the values you've been given.

Target AO3

5   A student is doing an investigation into the properties of a transformer. They want to determine how the output potential difference, V_o, is related to the ratio of the number of turns on the secondary coil, N_s, to the number of turns on the primary coil, N_p.

The student constructs a basic transformer from a square iron core and two lengths of insulated wire. They then connect each coil to a circuit, as shown in **Figure 2**. The input potential difference, V_i, of 1.2 V is provided by an alternating power supply.

Before starting the experiment, the student notices that the insulation on the secondary coil has been worn through, and so she replaces the wire with an undamaged one.

Figure 2

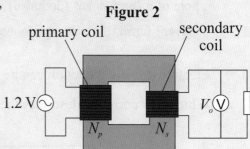

a) Give **two** reasons why it is important that the wire is replaced.

....

....

....

[2]

The student carries out her experiment, and plots her results on a graph of V_o against the ratio $\frac{N_s}{N_p}$, as shown in **Figure 3**.

b) Calculate the gradient of the graph in **Figure 3**.

gradient = ... V

[2]

Figure 3

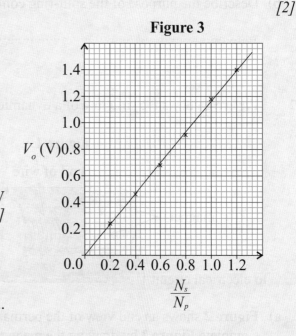

c) State and explain whether the results in **Figure 3** agree with the relationship $\frac{V_o}{V_i} = \frac{N_s}{N_p}$.

....

....

....

....

....

[3]

[Total 7 marks]

Exam Tip

When working out the gradient of a line, start off by drawing a right-angled triangle with your line as the longest side. Your triangle should cover more than half the length of the line. Next, write down the coordinates of the points on your line that are also the corners of the triangle. You can then use these coordinates to work out the gradient of the line.

Section 8 — Electric and Magnetic Fields

Generators, Microphones and Loudspeakers

For each option, circle the word to correctly describe how loudspeakers work.

A(n) (alternating / direct) current is passed through a coil of wire that is wrapped around one pole of a (permanent / induced) magnet and attached to the base of a paper cone. When a current flows, the coil experiences a (force / moment) which makes the paper cone move.

1 Electromagnetic induction can be used to create a current in dynamos and alternators.

a) Which row correctly describes the current produced by dynamos and alternators?

		Dynamo	Alternator
☐	**A**	a.c.	a.c.
☐	**B**	d.c.	d.c.
☐	**C**	a.c.	d.c.
☐	**D**	d.c.	a.c.

[1]

b) Describe the purpose of the split-ring commutator in a dynamo.

....

[1]

[Total 2 marks]

2 **Figure 1** shows the structure of a dynamic microphone.

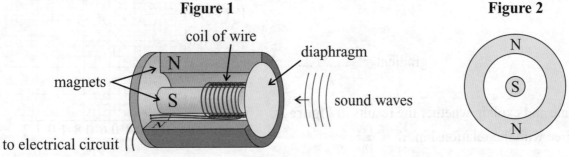

Figure 1

Figure 2

a) **Figure 2** shows an end view of the permanent magnet inside of the microphone. Complete **Figure 2** by drawing the magnetic field lines for the microphone.

[2]

b) Explain how the microphone converts sound waves to electrical signals.

....

....

....

....

....

[4]

[Total 6 marks]

Generating and Distributing Electricity

Warm-Up

Use the words in the box to label the diagram showing electricity generation in a power station.

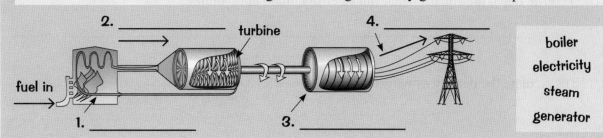

2. _____ turbine   4. _____

fuel in

1. _____   3. _____

boiler
electricity
steam
generator

1   A transformer has 12 turns on its the primary coil. An input p.d. of 245 V is converted to an output p.d. of 84 V. Calculate the number of turns on the secondary coil. Give your answer to 2 significant figures.

Number of turns = ...
[Total 4 marks]

2*   Electricity produced in power stations is transmitted to people's homes by the national grid. The national grid often transmits electricity at 400 000 V.

Explain the advantages of using transformers and high-voltage cables to transfer large amounts of energy every second via the national grid. You should use equations to justify your answer.

....
....
....
....
....
....
....
....
....
....
....
....
....

[Total 6 marks]

Density

1   A 0.5 m³ block of tungsten has a mass of 10 000 kg.

    a) i) Write down the equation that links density, mass and volume.

....
[1]

       ii) Calculate the density of tungsten.

Density = ... kg/m³
[2]

    b) Calculate the mass of a 0.02 m³ sample cut from the tungsten block.

Mass = ... kg
[2]
[Total 5 marks]

2   The titanium bar shown in **Figure 1** has a mass of 90.0 kg.

Figure 1

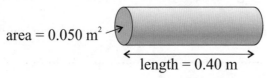

area = 0.050 m²

length = 0.40 m

Calculate the density of titanium.

Density = ... kg/m³
[Total 3 marks]

3   A student uses the apparatus in **Figure 2** to calculate the volumes
    of different rings to determine what materials they are made from.

Figure 2

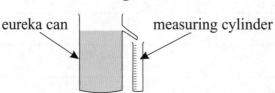

eureka can   measuring cylinder

The can is filled up to the spout so that when a ring is placed in the can, the displaced water flows into the measuring cylinder. **Figure 3** shows an incomplete table of the student's results.

Figure 3

Ring	Mass (g)	Water displaced (ml)	Material
A	5.7	0.30	....
B	2.7	0.60	....
C	3.0	0.30	....

One ring is made from gold, one is made from silver and the other is made from titanium.
Complete **Figure 3** using the following information:
Density of gold = 19 g/cm³   Density of silver = 10 g/cm³   Density of titanium = 4.5 g/cm³

[Total 5 marks]

PRACTICAL

4   **Figure 4** shows a density bottle. When full, the density bottle holds a set volume of liquid that is accurately known.

Figure 4

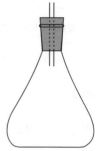

Describe how the student could use a density bottle and a mass balance to calculate the density of a small, irregularly-shaped object.

....

....

....

....

....

....

....

....

....

....

[Total 6 marks]

Section 9 — Matter

Kinetic Theory and States of Matter

The images below show the particles in a substance when it is in three different states of matter. Label each image to show whether the substance is a solid, a liquid or a gas.

....

1 Draw a line to match the change of state on the left to its description on the right. *(Grade 4-6)*

condensation	gas to liquid
sublimation	liquid to gas
evaporation	solid to gas

[Total 1 mark]

2 The density of different states of matter varies. *(Grade 4-6)*

a) Which of the following statements is true about the different states of matter?

☐ **A** A liquid is usually less dense than a gas.

☐ **B** A liquid is usually more dense than a solid.

☐ **C** A solid is usually more dense than a gas.

☐ **D** A solid is usually less dense than a gas.

[1]

b) A student notices that ice cubes float when he puts them into a glass of water. This is because ice is less dense than liquid water. Explain what this suggests about the arrangement of the water molecules in each state.

....

....

....

....

[2]

[Total 3 marks]

3 A student leaves a sealed glass flask with 200 ml of purified water in it on a windowsill on a hot day. He checks the flask every hour and observes that the volume of liquid water decreases throughout the day.

Grade 4-6

a) Suggest why the volume of liquid water has decreased during the day.

....

[1]

b) Explain what happens to the total mass of the bottle and its contents during the day.

....

....

....

[2]

[Total 3 marks]

4 A student does an experiment to investigate methanol as it changes state. **Figure 1** shows their equipment. When the water bath is turned on, the water inside it begins to heat up.

Grade 6-7

Figure 1

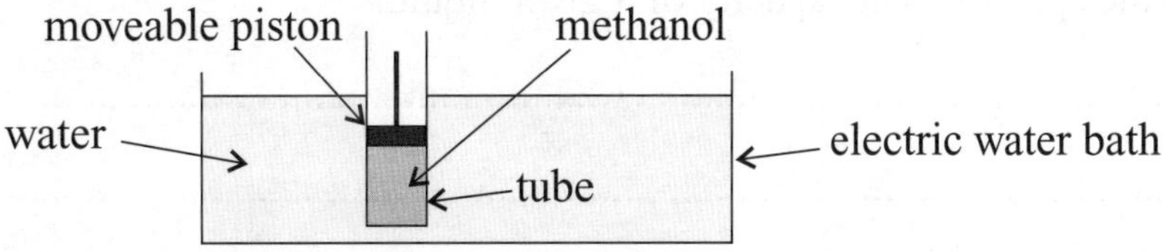

moveable piston   methanol

water →   ← electric water bath

← tube

As the water is heated, the piston begins to move upwards. After a short time, the tube containing the methanol begins to fill with gas. Explain this behaviour in terms of the energy transfers and the particles that make up the methanol.

....

....

....

....

....

....

....

....

[Total 5 marks]

Exam Tip

Remember that all changes of state are physical changes, not chemical changes. Chemical changes result in a new substance being created. During a change of state, the particles in a substance move and either get closer together or further apart. The particles themselves don't change, so a change of state has to be a physical change.

Section 9 — Matter

Specific Heat Capacity

Which of the following is the correct definition of specific heat capacity? Tick **one** box.

The energy transferred when an object is burnt. ☐

The maximum amount of energy an object can store before it melts. ☐

The energy needed to raise 1 kg of a substance by 10 °C. ☐

The energy needed to raise 1 kg of a substance by 1 °C. ☐

1　A student is measuring the specific heat capacity of different liquids. (Grade 6-7) **PRACTICAL**

For each liquid, she connects an immersion heater in a circuit with an ammeter, a voltmeter and a power supply. She also uses a thermometer, mass balance and stopwatch. She puts the immersion heater in the liquid and measures the potential difference across and current through the immersion heater as it heats.

a) i) The student measures the temperature of each liquid before and after it is heated. Give **two** other values that the student would need to measure to find the specific heat capacity of a given liquid.

1. ....

2. ....

[2]

ii) Explain how the student would calculate the specific heat capacity from her measurements. Use equations from the equation sheet on page 156.

....

....

....

....

[3]

b) Each sample was heated to raise its temperature by 10 °C. The student then recorded her results, shown in **Figure 1**. Complete **Figure 1** to show the specific heat capacity of liquid C.

Figure 1

Liquid	Mass (kg)	Energy supplied (kJ)	Specific heat capacity (J/kg °C)
A	0.30	12.6	4200
B	0.30	6.6	2200
C	0.30	6.0	....

[3]

[Total 8 marks]

Target AO3

2 A student is testing three materials, A, B and C, to find their specific heat capacities. **Grade 7-9**

He heats a 100 g block of each material using an electric heater. The heater is connected to a joulemeter, which measures the amount of energy transferred to the block.
The student measures the temperature of each block for every 250 J of energy transferred.
Each block of material is wrapped in a layer of silicone foam while it is heated.

a) The student says, "Putting foam around the blocks while they are heated will improve the accuracy of my results." State and explain whether the student is correct.

....

....

....
[2]

A graph of the student's results for the three materials is shown in **Figure 2**.

Figure 2

b) Using the graph, explain which material has the greatest specific heat capacity.

....

....

....

....

....
[3]

c) Explain how the student can determine whether his results are valid.

....

....

....
[2]

[Total 7 marks]

Exam Tip

You may be asked to analyse the effect that using a particular piece of equipment, or method of measurement, will have on the quality of the experiment. It might help to think through how you've seen it used in other experiments.

Specific Latent Heat

1   **Figure 1** shows the mass and specific latent heat of vaporisation (SLH) of substances A-D. Which substance requires the most amount of energy to completely boil it?

Figure 1

	Mass (kg)	SLH (J/kg)
☐ A	1	1.5
☐ B	1	1.0
☐ C	2	1.5
☐ D	3	2.0

[Total 1 mark]

2   A student uses a freezer to freeze 0.50 kg of brine.

a) Define the term 'specific latent heat'.

....

....
[1]

b) Explain the difference between specific heat capacity and specific latent heat.

....

....
[1]

Figure 2 shows the temperature-time graph for brine as it was cooled.

Figure 2

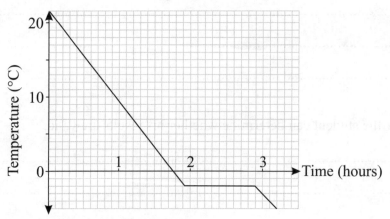

c) State the freezing point of brine.

Freezing point = ... °C
[1]

[Total 3 marks]

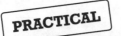

3 A student investigates the specific latent heat of water. They place 500 g of ice into an insulated beaker and use an immersion heater to heat the ice. They record the temperature of the water every 10 seconds. Their results are shown in **Figure 3**.

Figure 3

Time (s)	Temperature (°C)
0	0
10	0
20	0
30	0
40	0
50	0
60	7
70	21

Time (s)	Temperature (°C)
80	36
90	50
100	64
110	79
120	92
130	100
140	100
150	100

Figure 4

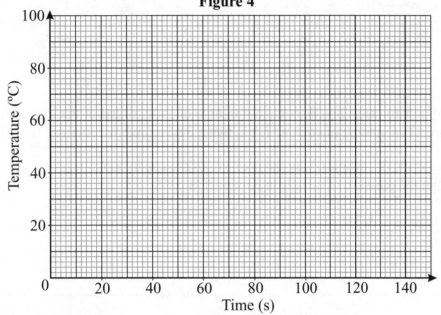

a) Draw the temperature-time graph for the student's results on **Figure 4**.

[2]

b) The immersion heater transfers 1.13 MJ of energy to the water once it has reached its boiling point to completely boil all of the water.
Calculate the specific latent heat of vaporisation of water. Give your answer in MJ/kg.

Specific latent heat = ... MJ/kg

[3]

c) Explain, in terms of particles, the shape of the graph between 0 and 50 seconds.

....

....

....

[3]

[Total 8 marks]

Section 9 — Matter

Particle Motion in Gases

Circle the correct words or phrases below so that the sentences are correct.

The particles in a gas are always moving in <u>the same direction / random directions</u>.

A gas exerts a force on a container due to <u>collisions / radioactivity</u>.

The total force exerted by the particles per unit area is the gas <u>energy / pressure</u>.

1 Describe, in terms of particles, what is meant by the term absolute zero. (Grade 4-6)

....

....

....

[Total 1 mark]

2 Two sealed containers, A and B, contain the same quantity of gas at the same temperature. The volume of container A is twice the volume of container B. (Grade 6-7)

Explain, in terms of particles, why the pressure of the gas in container A is lower than the pressure of the gas in container B.

....

....

....

....

[Total 2 marks]

3 A gas is held in a sealed container with a fixed volume. The initial temperature of the gas is 295 K. (Grade 6-7)

a) Give the initial temperature of the gas in degrees Celsius.

.... °C

[1]

b) The container is heated over a Bunsen burner.
Describe and explain how this affects the pressure of the gas inside the container.

....

....

....

[3]

[Total 4 marks]

4   **Figure 1** shows four sealed containers. Each contains the same mass of a gas. In which container is the pressure of the gas the highest?

Figure 1

Volume = 0.04 m³   Volume = 0.04 m³   Volume = 40 000 cm³   Volume = 40 000 cm³
Temperature = 10 °C   Temperature = 20 °C   Temperature = 283 K   Temperature = 30 °C

☐ A   ☐ B   ☐ C   ☐ D

[Total 1 mark]

5   A student investigates how varying the volume of a container full of a fixed mass of gas at a constant temperature affects the pressure of the gas. **Figure 2** is an incomplete table of his results.

Figure 2

Volume (m³)	Pressure (kPa)
8.0×10^{-4}	50
4.0×10^{-4}	100
2.5×10^{-4}	160
1.6×10^{-4}	....

Figure 3

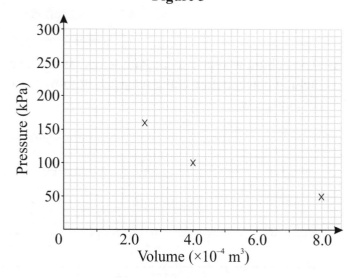

a) Complete **Figure 2** by calculating the missing pressure measurement.

[3]

b) Using information from **Figure 2**, complete the graph in **Figure 3** by plotting the missing data and drawing a line of best fit.

[2]

[Total 5 marks]

Exam Tip

Remember, one degree on the Kelvin scale is the same size as one degree on the Celsius scale, but O K is much, much colder than O °C. A temperature in Kelvin will always have a higher value than the same temperature in Celsius.

Pressure, Temperature and Volume

1   Put a tick in the box next to the row that correctly
    describes the forces produced by the particles in a gas.

		Direction of force exerted by each particle	Direction of net force exerted by the gas
☐	A	in a random direction compared to the walls of the container	parallel to the walls of the container
☐	B	at right-angles to the walls of the container	parallel to the walls of the container
☐	C	at right-angles to the walls of the container	in a random direction compared to the walls of the container
☐	D	in a random direction compared to the walls of the container	at right-angles to the walls of the container

[Total 1 mark]

2   **Figure 1** shows a syringe filled with helium gas and sealed with a plunger and a bung.

Figure 1

bung   moveable plunger

helium gas

a) The helium is kept at a constant temperature. The plunger is pulled out a short distance and
    held in place, before being released. It moves a short distance back down the syringe and stops.
    Explain why.

    ....

    ....

    ....

    ....

    ....

    ....

[5]

b) The plunger is then pushed in, compressing the helium.
    Suggest why the temperature of the helium might change.

    ....

    ....

    ....

    ....

    ....

[4]

[Total 9 marks]

Forces and Elasticity

1 A child is playing with a toy that contains a spring. *Grade 4-6*

a) Give the minimum number of forces that need to be applied to the spring in order to stretch it.

....
[1]

b) When the spring is compressed, it distorts elastically.
Explain the difference between elastic and inelastic distortion.

....

....

....
[2]

c) i) State the equation that links the force exerted on a spring, its spring constant and its extension.

....
[1]

ii) A 20 N force stretches the spring by 8 cm. Calculate the spring constant of the spring.

Spring constant = ... N/m
[2]

d) State **one** assumption you made to answer part c) ii).

....
[1]

[Total 7 marks]

2 **Figure 1** shows a piece of elastic being stretched between two pieces of wood. The spring constant of the elastic is 50 N/m and the unstretched length of the elastic is 3.1 cm. *Grade 6-7*

Figure 1

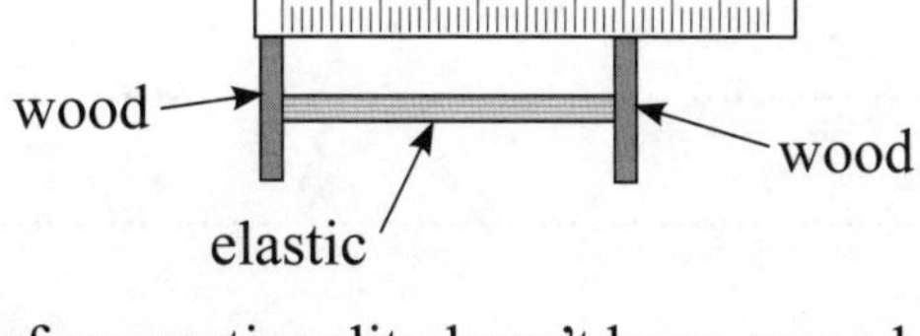

Given that the limit of proportionality hasn't been exceeded,
how much energy is stored in the stretched elastic?

☐ **A** 2.89×10^{-2} J   ☐ **B** 289 J   ☐ **C** 2.25 J   ☐ **D** 2.25×10^{-4} J

[Total 1 mark]

PRACTICAL

3 A student investigated the relationship between the extension of a spring and the forces acting on it. He hung different weights from the bottom of the spring and measured its extension with a ruler, as shown in **Figure 2**.

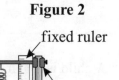

Figure 2

a) **Figure 3** shows the results that the student obtained in his investigation. Draw the force-extension graph for the student's results on the axes in **Figure 4**.

Figure 3

Force (N)	Extension (cm)
0.0	0.0
1.0	4.4
2.0	7.5
3.0	12.3
4.0	16.0
5.0	22.2
6.0	32.0

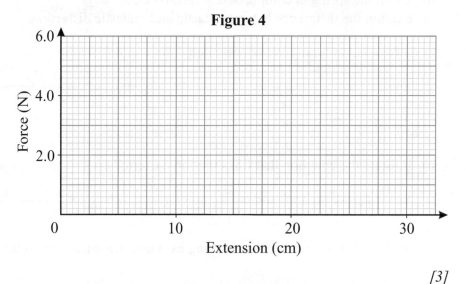

[3]

b) Using the graph you have drawn, calculate the spring constant of the spring being tested.

Spring constant = ... N/m

[2]

c) The student realised he had stretched the spring past its limit of proportionality. Explain how you can tell this from the graph.

....

....

[2]

d) The student removed the masses from the spring. Whilst he unloaded the spring, he measured its extension for each force again. He found that, when unloading the spring, the extension of the spring was 20.1 cm when a force of 4.0 N acted on it. Suggest and explain a reason for this.

....

....

....

[2]

[Total 9 marks]

Exam Tip

It's easy to get caught out by problems like question 2. Remember, for the equations for stretching (or compressing), you need to use the amount the length of an object has changed by, not its total length after it's been stretched.

Fluid Pressure

1   Water in the chamber of a water pistol is squeezed out when a force is applied by the plunger. A force of 12 N is applied by a plunger with a surface area of 0.15 m². **Grade 6-7**

a) State the equation that links pressure, force and area.

....

[1]

b) Calculate the pressure exerted by the plunger.

Pressure = ... Pa

[2]

[Total 3 marks]

2   A student fills a container with different liquids, and each time places a pressure sensor in the liquid, as shown in **Figure 3**. The sensor is held at a depth of 15 cm in each liquid. **Grade 7-9**

Figure 3

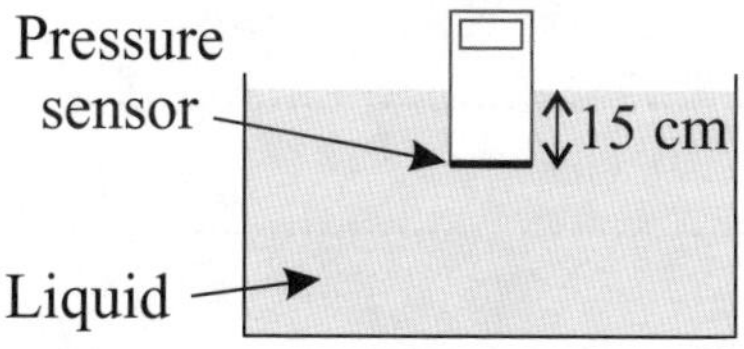

Pressure sensor

15 cm

Liquid

Figure 4

Liquid	Density (kg/m³)	Pressure due to liquid (Pa)
Water	1000	1500
Liquid B	....	2850

a) Complete the table in **Figure 4** by calculating the density of liquid B.
Gravitational field strength = 10 N/kg.

[3]

b) Using the particle model, explain why the pressure caused by liquid B is larger than the pressure caused by water for any given depth of the liquids in the containers.

....

....

....

....

....

....

....

[4]

[Total 7 marks]

Section 9 — Matter

Upthrust and Atmospheric Pressure

1 **Figure 1** shows a digital force gauge being used to measure the weight of a golf ball in air and whilst it is placed in water. *(Grade 6-7)*

Explain why the weight of the golf ball appears to change when it is placed in the water.

Figure 1
force gauge → 0.45 N | 0.30 N
golf ball → ○ | ○ ← water

[Total 3 marks]

2 A boat is sailing across the ocean. A silver necklace is dropped over the side, and sinks. *(Grade 7-9)*

Explain why the boat floats on the water, but the necklace sinks.

[Total 5 marks]

3* Explain why atmospheric pressure decreases with altitude. *(Grade 7-9)*

[Total 6 marks]

Section 9 — Matter

Mixed Questions

1 A ray of light in a vacuum travels 1 foot in around 1 nanosecond.

a) A foot is a measure of distance. State the SI unit for measuring distance.

....
[1]

b) One nanosecond is equal to

☐ **A** 1×10^9 seconds.   ☐ **C** 1×10^{-6} seconds.

☐ **B** 1×10^{-9} seconds.   ☐ **D** 1×10^{-6} seconds.

[1]

c) Distance and time are both scalar quantities. State what is meant by a scalar quantity.

....

....
[1]

[Total 3 marks]

2 A child pulls a toy along the ground. There is friction between the toy's wheels and the ground. The forces acting on the toy are shown in **Figure 1**.

Figure 1

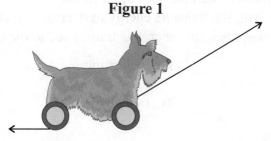

a) Which of the following shows the correct way to find the resultant force acting on the toy from a scale drawing of the forces acting on it? The dashed lines represent the forces acting on the toy, and the solid line represents the resultant force.

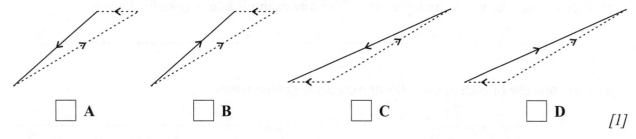

☐ **A**   ☐ **B**   ☐ **C**   ☐ **D**

[1]

b) The total horizontal force acting on the toy is 5 N to the right. Calculate the work done by the child as she pulls it a distance of 10 m to the right. Use the equation:

work done = force × distance moved in the direction of the force.

Work done = ... J
[2]

[Total 3 marks]

126

3 A girl is walking her dog. She decides to record the distance she had travelled during the walk every 5 minutes. *(Grade 4-6)*

a) She uses the information she collected to draw a distance/time graph for her walk.
What does the gradient of a distance/time graph represent?

☐ **A** speed

☐ **B** acceleration

☐ **C** distance

☐ **D** deceleration

[1]

b) After exactly 5 minutes, she has walked a distance of 420 m.
Calculate the average speed at which she walked. Use the equation:

average speed = distance travelled ÷ time.

Give the unit in your answer.

Average speed = ... Unit: ....

[3]

c) Whilst walking, the girl throws a ball for her dog to chase.
Each time she throws the ball, she transfers energy to the ball's kinetic energy store.
Which method correctly describes how energy is transferred to the ball?

☐ **A** electrically   ☐ **C** by heating

☐ **B** mechanically   ☐ **D** by radiation

[1]

[Total 5 marks]

4 X-rays and gamma rays are types of electromagnetic waves. *(Grade 4-6)*

a) Electromagnetic waves are transverse. Give **one** example of a longitudinal wave.

....

[1]

b) State **one** use of each of the following electromagnetic waves.

X-ray: ....

Gamma rays: ....

[2]

c) The equation shows a nucleus emitting a gamma ray. $^{99}_{43}\text{Tc} \rightarrow {}^{A}_{43}\text{Tc} + {}^{B}_{0}\gamma$
Determine the values of A and B.

A = ...   B = ...

[2]

[Total 5 marks]

Mixed Questions

PRACTICAL

5   A student tests the relationship between potential difference and current for a diode.   **Grade 4-6**

a) Which of the following is the circuit symbol for a diode?

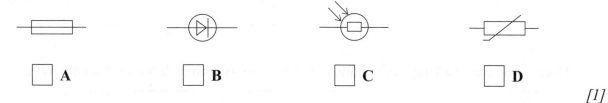

☐ **A**   ☐ **B**   ☐ **C**   ☐ **D**

[1]

b) Which of the following shows an *I-V* graph for a diode?

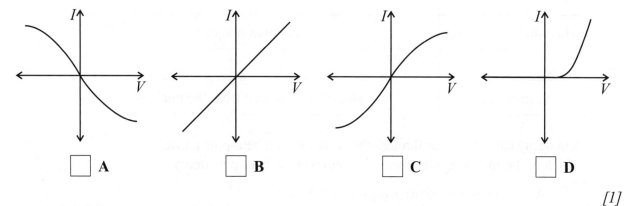

☐ **A**   ☐ **B**   ☐ **C**   ☐ **D**

[1]

At a potential difference of 0.7 V the current through a diode is 0.1 A.

c) i) State the equation that links potential difference, current and resistance.

....

[1]

ii) Calculate the resistance of the diode.

Resistance = ... Ω

[2]

[Total 5 marks]

6   Electromagnetic waves are able to travel through a vacuum.   **Grade 6-7**

a) In a vacuum, an infrared wave has a wavelength of 1×10^{-6} m and a frequency of 3×10^{14} Hz. Calculate the speed of the infrared wave in a vacuum. Give your answer in standard form.

Speed = ... m/s

[4]

b) Determine the speed at which radio waves travel in a vacuum.

....

[1]

[Total 5 marks]

Mixed Questions

7   Radiation is around us all the time.   (Grade 6-7)

a) Radioactivity can be measured in different ways.
   Suggest **one** method that could be used to measure the radioactivity of a source.

   ....

   [1]

b) Draw a line from each type of radiation on the left to its correct description on the right.

alpha particle		an electromagnetic wave

beta-minus particle		a helium nucleus

gamma ray		an electron emitted from the nucleus

[1]

c) Beta decay can also occur through the emission of a beta-plus particle.
   Which of the following statements is **incorrect** for beta-plus decay?

   ☐   **A**   A neutron becomes a proton in the nucleus.

   ☐   **B**   A positron is emitted from the nucleus.

   ☐   **C**   A proton becomes a neutron in the nucleus.

   ☐   **D**   The mass number of the nucleus remains the same.

   [1]

d) i) The term 'activity' can be used when describing a radioactive source.
      State what is meant by activity and give the unit it is measured in.

      ....
      [2]

   ii) On the axes in **Figure 2**, sketch how the
       activity of a radioactive source varies over time.

       Figure 2

       (axes: vertical "Activity", horizontal "Time")

       [2]

e) The term 'half-life' can also be used when describing a source of radiation.
   State what is meant by half-life. You should refer to activity in your answer.

   ....

   ....
   [1]

   [Total 8 marks]

Mixed Questions

8 A battery powered winch is used to raise a 40.0 kg crate vertically off the ground.

a) Complete **Figure 3** to show the main energy transfers that occur as the crate is lifted.

Figure 3

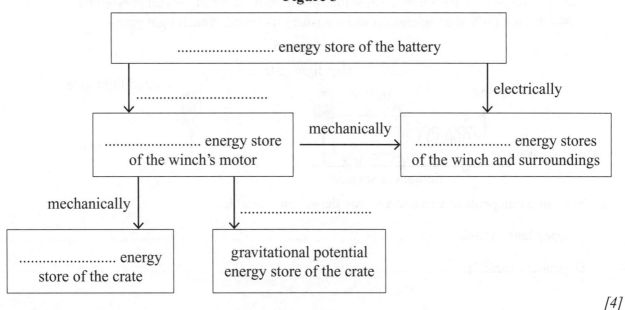

.... energy store of the battery

electrically

....

.... energy store
of the winch's motor

mechanically

.... energy stores
of the winch and surroundings

mechanically

....

.... energy
store of the crate

gravitational potential
energy store of the crate

[4]

b) The crate is raised 1.1 m vertically off the ground.
Calculate the energy transferred to the crate's gravitational potential energy store.

Energy transferred = ... J

[4]

[Total 8 marks]

9 A 10 cm × 10 cm × 10 cm cube of material A is placed in a beaker of water.
It floats when 7 cm of the cube is submerged in the water, as shown in **Figure 4**.

a) i) State the equation that links density,
mass and volume.

Figure 4

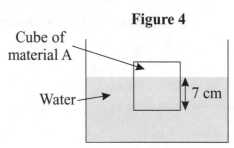

Cube of
material A

Water

7 cm

....

[1]

ii) Water has a density of 1000 kg/m³.
Calculate the mass of the water displaced by the cube.

Mass = ... kg

[3]

b) The water exerts an upwards force of 7 N on the cube so that it floats.
Calculate the pressure of the water acting on the bottom face of the cube.

Pressure = ... Pa

[4]

[Total 8 marks]

Mixed Questions

10 A student is investigating how the deceleration of a 0.50 kg trolley varies based on the surface it is travelling on. Her set-up is shown in **Figure 5**.

The student uses a spring attached to the wall to provide the driving force for the trolley. She pushes the trolley against the spring until the spring is compressed by 0.040 m each time, then releases it and measures its speed at each light gate.

Figure 5

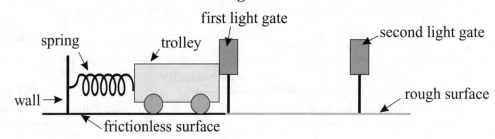

a) State **one** independent variable and **one** dependent variable.

Independent variable: ....

Dependent variable: ....

[2]

After the spring is released, the first light gate records the trolley's speed just after it leaves the spring. Its speed is found to be 0.60 m/s. You can assume that no friction acts upon the trolley between it leaving the spring and it passing through the first light gate.

b) i) Calculate the energy in the spring's elastic potential energy store when it is compressed.

Energy = ... J

[3]

Between the two light gates, a constant frictional force acts on the trolley. The distance between the two light gates is 1.00 m and the speed of the trolley at the second light gate is 0.40 m/s.

ii) Calculate the deceleration of the trolley as it travels between the two light gates.

Deceleration = ... m/s^2

[3]

The student replaces the rough surface with a frictionless board. The trolley travels along the frictionless board with a speed of 0.60 m/s until it collides with a second, stationary trolley that has a mass of 0.40 kg. The first trolley stops moving and the second trolley moves off.

c) Calculate the velocity at which the second trolley moves after the collision.

Velocity = ... m/s

[4]

[Total 12 marks]

11 A student is designing a basic electronic toy. He wants the toy to be able to light up and spin around. He creates a basic circuit of a battery connected to a motor. In parallel to the motor, he connects two filament bulbs and a fixed resistor. The two bulbs and the resistor are all in series with each other. The bulbs and the motor can be switched on and off separately.

Grade 7-9

a) Draw the circuit diagram for the circuit created by the student.

[5]

b) The student notices that if the circuit is left on for a long period of time, the resistor and the motor both get hot. Explain the causes of this and suggest **one** way of reducing this heating.

....

....

....

....

....

....

....

[4]

c) The student turns on only the motor. The potential difference across the motor is 6.0 V and a current of 70 mA flows through the motor. After 10 minutes, the student switches off the motor and measures the temperature of the coil of wire inside the motor. He finds that it has increased by 25 °C since it was first turned on.

3.0 g of wire makes up the coil inside the motor.
The material it is made from has a specific heat capacity of 400 J/kg °C.

Calculate the amount of energy that is usefully transferred by the motor in 10 minutes. You can assume that all energy not transferred to thermal energy stores is usefully transferred. Give your answer to 2 significant figures.

Energy transferred usefully = ... J

[5]

[Total 14 marks]

Mixed Questions

12   **Figure 6** shows a Van de Graaff generator which is used to create a positively charged metal dome.

Figure 6

The Van de Graaff generator consists of a metal dome and a belt made of insulating material wrapped round two wheels. The wheels turn in order to turn the belt.

The bottom of the belt continuously brushes past metal comb A which is positively charged. The top of the belt continuously brushes past metal comb B, which is attached to the metal dome.

a) Explain why the belt must be made of insulating material.

....

....

[2]

b) Explain how a charge builds up on the dome.

....

....

....

....

....

[4]

c) i) An earthed piece of metal is brought near the sphere. A spark is created between the dome and the piece of metal. Describe this behaviour in terms of the movement of electrons.

....

....

[1]

ii) Just before the spark, a charge of 15 μC has built up on the dome and the potential difference between the dome and the earthed metal is 320 kV. Calculate the energy transferred by the spark.

Energy = ... J

[4]

[Total 11 marks]

Mixed Questions

13   An astronomer is studying a nearby red giant.
      He uses a telescope mounted on a satellite orbiting Earth.   (Grade 7-9)

a) Suggest a reason why the telescope is used in space, and not on Earth.

....

[1]

b) As a star transitions from a main sequence star to a red giant, its colour changes
    from white to red. State and explain what you can deduce about the
    temperature of the star as it transitions from a main sequence star to a red giant.

....

....

....

[3]

c) i) The astronomer measures the peak wavelength of the radiation emitted from the red giant to be
        infrared radiation. The results have been red-shifted. Deduce the part of the electromagnetic
        spectrum that the peak radiation originally emitted by the red giant came from.

....

[1]

    ii) During a star's red giant stage, some of the nuclei within the star are undergoing fusion.
        The astronomer suggests that because of this, its mass is decreasing.
        Explain whether or not the astronomer is correct.

....

....

....

[2]

A second astronomer is studying   **Figure 7**
nearby planets, described in **Figure 7**.

Planet	Diameter (km)	Mass (× 10^{24} kg)
A	7000	4.9
B	7000	6.4

d) Two identical artificial satellites are sent to orbit and investigate both planets.
    Both satellites are in stable orbits at the same height above their planet's surface.
    Explain whether or not there is a difference in the speed at which each satellite orbits its planet.

....

....

....

....

....

....

[4]

[Total 11 marks]

Mixed Questions

14 **Figure 8** shows a basic model of how the national grid uses step-up and step-down transformers to vary the potential difference and current of the electricity it transmits.

Figure 8

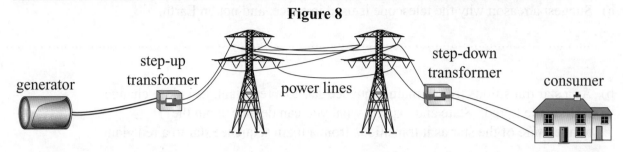

a) A power station's generator produces electricity at a potential difference of 25 kV and a current of 4000 A. It is connected to the national grid by a step-up transformer that has 1000 turns on its primary coil and 16 000 turns on its secondary coil. You can assume that the transformer is 100% efficient. Calculate the current of the electricity transmitted by the national grid.

Current = ... A
[4]

b) Each minute, 34.92 GJ of energy is transferred to the generator.
   Calculate the efficiency of the generator, assuming its power output is constant.

Efficiency = ...%
[5]

[Total 9 marks]

15 Both hydro-electric and nuclear power stations can be used to generate electricity.

Figure 9 shows a reservoir — water held back by a dam. A pumped-storage hydro-electric power plant, shown in **Figure 10**, can use a reservoir to generate electricity.

Figure 9   **Figure 10**

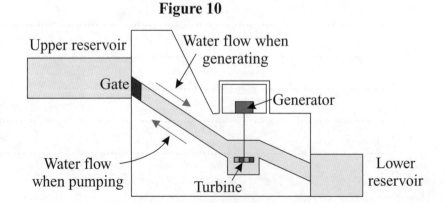

When generating electricity, the gate is opened and water flows from the upper to the lower reservoir. This turns the turbine which is connected to an electricity generator.

During times of low demand, electricity is used to turn the turbine and pump water from the lower reservoir back to the higher reservoir, ready to respond to peaks in electrical demand.

a) Describe the energy transfers that occur in a pumped-storage hydro-electric power plant while it generates electricity.

....

....

....

....

....

....

[5]

b)* Fission reactions in nuclear power stations produce nuclear waste. One radioactive isotope in nuclear waste is caesium-137. Caesium-137 has a half-life of 30 years. It produces beta and gamma radiation as it decays. Explain the safety implications of storing the nuclear waste produced by the plant and the precautions needed to reduce the risks posed by storing nuclear waste.

....

....

....

....

....

....

....

....

....

....

....

....

[6]

[Total 11 marks]

Mixed Questions

Answers

Section 1 — Motion and Forces

Pages 1-2 — Distance, Displacement, Speed and Velocity

Warm-up

Scalar — mass, time, temperature

Vector — acceleration, weight, force

1   C *[1 mark]*

2   340 m/s *[1 mark]*

3 a)   7 m *[1 mark]*

   b)   12 m *[1 mark]*

   c)

A   C   B

      [1 mark for arrow of correct length in the correct direction]

   d)   2 m *[1 mark]*

4 a)   distance travelled = average speed × time *[1 mark]*

   b)   22 minutes = 22 × 60 = 1320 s

       distance travelled = average speed × time

                      = 4.0 × 1320 = 5280 m

       5280 m = 5280 ÷ 1000 = 5.28 km = **5.3 km (to 2 s.f.)**

       [4 marks for correct answer to two significant figures, otherwise 1 mark for correctly converting the time into seconds, 1 mark for correctly substituting the numbers into the equation, 1 mark for correct numerical answer for distance travelled]

5 a)   distance travelled = average speed × time

       Typical walking speed = 1.4 m/s (accept 1-2 m/s)

       time = distance travelled ÷ average speed

            = 3500 ÷ 1.4 = **2500 s** (accept 1750-3500 s)

       [4 marks for correct answer, otherwise 1 mark for stating the correct equation, 1 mark for using a suitable estimate for walking speed, 1 mark for correctly substituting the numbers into the equation]

   b)   Typical cycling speed = 5.5 m/s (accept 4.5-6.5 m/s)

       distance travelled = average speed × time, so:

       time = distance travelled ÷ average speed = 3500 ÷ 5.5

                                = 636.363... s

       2500 − 636.363... = 1863.636... s

                    = **2000 s (to 1 s.f.)** (accept 1000-3000 s)

       [4 marks for correct answer, otherwise 1 mark for using a suitable estimate for cycling speed, 1 mark for correctly substituting the numbers into the equation, 1 mark for subtracting from the answer to part a)]

   c)   time = 15 × 60 = 900 s, 7.2 km = 7200 m

       distance travelled = average speed × time, so:

       average speed = distance travelled ÷ time

                   = 7200 ÷ 900 = **8 m/s**

       [3 marks for correct answer, otherwise 1 mark for correctly converting the time into seconds and km into m, 1 mark for correctly substituting the numbers into the equation]

Pages 3-4 — Acceleration

Warm-up

A sprinter starting a race — 1.5 m/s²

A falling object — 10 m/s²

A bullet shot from a gun — 2 × 10⁵ m/s²

1   It will be slowing down/decelerating *[1 mark]*

2 a) $a = (v - u) \div t$

       = (3.2 − 0) ÷ 8.0 = **0.4 m/s²**

       [3 marks for correct answer, otherwise 1 mark for using correct acceleration equation, 1 mark for correctly substituting the numbers into the equation]

   b) $a = (v - u) \div t$, so:

       $v = (a \times t) + u$

       = (0.4 × 6.0) + 3.2 = **5.6 m/s**

       [3 marks for correct answer, otherwise 1 mark for rearranging acceleration equation for final velocity, 1 mark for substituting the correct numbers into the equation]

3      $v^2 - u^2 = 2 \times a \times x$ so as x = height, and g = 10 m/s²

       height = $(v^2 - u^2) \div (2 \times a)$ = (12² − 0²) ÷ (2 × 10)

              = **7.2 m**

       [3 marks for correct answer, otherwise 1 mark for rearranging the equation for distance (height), 1 mark for substituting the correct numbers into the equation]

4 a)   1.2 km = 1200 m

       $v = \sqrt{(2 \times a \times x) + u^2}$

       $= \sqrt{(2 \times 0.25 \times 1200) + (5.0)^2}$

       = **25 m/s**

       [3 marks for correct answer, otherwise 1 mark for rearranging the equation for final velocity, 1 mark for substituting the correct numbers into the equation]

   b) $a = (v - u) \div t$, so:

       $t = (v - u) \div a$

       = (25 − 5.0) ÷ 0.25 = **80 s**

       [3 marks for correct answer, otherwise 1 mark for rearranging the equation correctly, 1 mark for correctly substituting the numbers into the equation]

5      $v^2 - u^2 = 2 \times a \times x$ so

       $a = (v^2 - u^2) \div (2 \times x)$ = (18² − 30²) ÷ (2 × 360)

       = −0.8 m/s²

       So deceleration = **0.8 m/s²**

       [3 marks for correct answer, otherwise 1 mark for rearranging the equation for acceleration, 1 mark for substituting the correct numbers into the equation]

6   21 × 1000 ÷ 60 ÷ 60 = 5.83... m/s

       Say it takes the cyclist 7 s to accelerate.

       acceleration = change in velocity ÷ time = 5.83... ÷ 7

                  = 0.832... = **0.8 m/s² (to 1 s.f.)**

       [3 marks for a correct answer using a time between 5 and 15 seconds, otherwise 1 mark for correctly converting the speed into m/s, 1 mark for an estimated time taken of 5-15 seconds]

You might have estimated the distance it took for the cyclist to get up to speed, then used $v^2 - u^2 = 2 \times a \times x$. As long as you used a sensible distance and correctly substituted your numbers into the equation, you'd still receive full marks.

Pages 5-6 — Distance/Time Graphs

1 a)

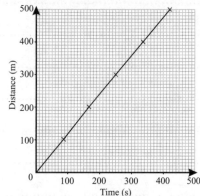

       [3 marks for graph plotted correctly, otherwise 1 mark for three points correct, 1 mark for a straight line going through all plotted points]

   b)   360 m (accept between 355 m and 365 m) *[1 mark]*

   c)   210 s (accept between 205 s and 215 s) *[1 mark]*

   d)   E.g. referring to the same point on the boat / making sure that the timings are measured from exactly level with the posts / making sure timings are made close to the posts to avoid parallax

       [1 mark for any correct answer]

2 a)   12 minutes *[1 mark]*

   b)   Accelerating *[1 mark]*

3 a)   Speed = gradient = (92 − 20) ÷ (6 − 3) = 72 ÷ 3 = **24 m/s**

       (accept between 23 m/s and 25 m/s)

       [3 marks for correct answer, otherwise 1 mark for stating that speed = gradient, 1 mark for a correct calculation attempting to find the gradient of the straight part of the d/t graph between 3 and 6 seconds]

   b)   Speed = gradient of a tangent to the line

              = (16 − 0) ÷ (3 − 1) = 16 ÷ 2 = **8 m/s**

              (accept between 6 m/s and 10 m/s)

       [3 marks for correct answer, otherwise 1 mark for a correct tangent to the line at 2 s, 1 mark for a correct calculation of the gradient of the tangent drawn]

Pages 7-8 — Velocity/Time Graphs

Warm-up

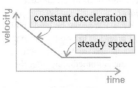
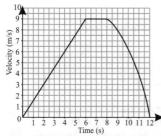

1   C *[1 mark]*
2   A *[1 mark]*
3 a)

[1 mark for correct shape of graph, 1 mark for graph ending at 0 m/s and 12 s]

b) $a = (v - u) \div t$ = gradient of the line
$a = (9 - 0) \div (6 - 0) = $ **1.5 m/s²**
[2 marks for correct answer, otherwise 1 mark for a correct method to calculate the gradient of the graph between 0 and 6 seconds]

c)   distance = speed × time = area under the line
0-6 s: area = ½ × base × height = ½ × 6 × 9 = 27 m
6-8 s: area = base × height = 2 × 9 = 18 m
Total distance in 8 s = 27 + 18 = **45 m**
[3 marks for correct answer, otherwise 1 mark for finding the area for 0-6 s, 1 mark for finding the area for 6-8 s]

d)   1 square is worth 0.5 s on the x-axis (time)
1 square is worth 0.5 m/s on the y-axis (velocity)
distance = speed × time = 0.5 × 0.5 = 0.25 m *[1 mark]*
Squares under the line between 8 s and 12 s = 91
[1 mark for a number that matches your graph ±5 squares]
91 × 0.25 = **22.75 m** *[1 mark for correctly multiplying your number of squares by your value of s]*

Pages 9-10 — Newton's First and Second Laws

Warm-up

Newton's <u>First</u> Law of motion says that an object will remain stationary or moving at <u>a constant velocity</u> if there is <u>a zero</u> resultant force acting on it. If there is <u>a non-zero</u> resultant force acting on the object, it will <u>accelerate</u>.

1 a)   A *[1 mark]*
$F = m \times a = 110\,000 \times 5.0 = 550\,000$ N

b)   There is no resultant force acting on the rocket (as there is no force from the thrusters or from friction) *[1 mark]*.

2   $F = m \times a$, so $m = F \div a = 38 \div 10 = $ **3.8 kg**
[3 marks for correct answer, otherwise 1 mark for giving the correct equation, 1 mark for substituting in the correct numbers]

3   $F = m \times a = 60 \times 0.4 = 24$ N
F = force from wind − drag force
So drag force = force from wind − F
= 44 − 24 = **20 N**
[4 marks for the correct answer, otherwise 1 mark for the correct equation, 1 mark for substituting the correct numbers into the equation, 1 mark for the correct resultant force]

4 a)   E.g. very large decelerations can cause serious injuries *[1 mark]*. This is because a larger acceleration requires a larger force (since $F = m \times a$) *[1 mark]*.

b)   The car comes to a stop in ~1 s (accept 0.5-2 s).
$a = (v - u) \div t = (0 - 14) \div 1 = -14$ m/s²
Mass of the car ~1000 kg (accept 600-2000 kg)
$F = m \times a = 1000 \times -14 = -14\,000$ N
So the resultant force is about **14 000 N** (accept 8000-28 000 N).
[5 marks for correct answer, otherwise 1 mark for correctly estimating the time taken to stop, 1 mark for using the correct acceleration equation and estimating the acceleration, 1 mark for correctly estimating the mass of the car, 1 mark for stating $F = m \times a$]

5   Typical speed of a lorry is 25 m/s
(accept 20-30 m/s)
$v^2 - u^2 = 2 \times a \times x$
$a = (v^2 - u^2) \div (2 \times x) = (0^2 - 25^2) \div (2 \times 50)$
$= -625 \div 100 = -6.25$ m/s² (accept 4-9 m/s²)
$F = m \times a = 7520 \times -6.25$
= **(−) 47 000 N** (accept 30 100-67 700 N)
[5 marks for correct answer, otherwise 1 mark for correctly estimating the speed of the lorry, 1 mark for correctly substituting in the numbers into the acceleration equation, 1 mark for stating $F = m \times a$, 1 mark for correctly substituting in the numbers to calculate the force]

Pages 11-12 — Weight and Circular Motion

Warm-up

1) True   2) False   3) True   4) True

1 a)   Weight is the force acting on an object due to gravity/ a gravitational field *[1 mark]*.

b)   weight = mass of object × gravitational field strength
= 65 × 10 = **650 N**
[2 marks for correct answer, otherwise 1 mark for substituting in the correct numbers]

c) $W = m \times g$ for g:
$g = W \div m = 232 \div (65 + 80) = $ **1.6 N/kg**
[3 marks for correct answer, otherwise 1 mark for rearranging weight equation for g, 1 mark for the correct numerical value, 1 mark for the correct unit]

2   No — velocity is speed in a given direction *[1 mark]*. The satellite travels at a constant speed, but is always changing direction so its velocity is always changing *[1 mark]*.

3 a)   E.g. the standard mass may no longer have the same mass as it is labelled with *[1 mark]*.
This is because some of the rusted standard mass is made of a different substance (the rust) instead of pure iron as when it was originally measured and labelled. Also, the rust could flake off the standard mass, leaving it with a lower mass than before.

b) i)   Systematic error *[1 mark]*
ii)   The weight of the plastic tray will be included in each of the weight measurements, making them all too large by the same amount *[1 mark]*.

c) i)   E.g.

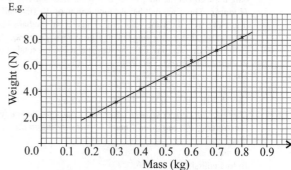

[1 mark for all points plotted correctly and 1 mark for a straight line of best fit drawn through or close to all points]

ii)   Since $W = mg$, by comparing this to the equation for a straight-line graph, $y = mx + c$, you can see that the gravitational field strength, g, is equal to the gradient of the graph, m *[1 mark]*.
E.g. $g = \dfrac{\text{change in } y}{\text{change in } x} = \dfrac{8.4 - 2.0}{0.82 - 0.18}$ *[1 mark]*
= **10 N/kg** *[1 mark]*
You'll get the calculation marks here as long as your calculation of the gradient is correct for your line of best fit.

Page 13 — Investigating Motion

1 a)   Any one from: e.g. using a light gate gets rid of the human error caused by reaction times when using a stopwatch / using a light gate is more accurate than a human using a stopwatch / a light gate can be directly linked to a data logger *[1 mark]*.

b)   E.g. she calculates the difference in the speed of the trolley between the two light gates and divides this by the time it took the trolley to travel between the light gates *[1 mark]*.

c) i) $F = m \times a$, so $a = F \div m$
= 1.5 ÷ 3 = **0.5 m/s²**
[3 marks for correct answer, otherwise 1 mark for rearranging the equation correctly, 1 mark for substituting in the correct numbers]
ii)   As the mass of the trolley is increased, the acceleration decreases *[1 mark]*

d) By finding the range of the results used to calculate that mean *[1 mark]* and then using uncertainty = range ÷ 2 *[1 mark]*.

Page 14 — Inertia and Newton's Third Law

Warm-up

When two objects interact, they exert equal and opposite forces on each other.

1 a) E.g. how difficult it is to change the velocity of an object / ratio of force over acceleration / $m = F \div a$
   [1 mark for any correct definition]

   b) Trolley B has the highest inertial mass *[1 mark]*, because it has the lowest velocity after the force has been applied, so its velocity is more difficult to change (than the velocities of the other trolleys) *[1 mark]*.

2 a) As the students push the wall, the wall will exert an equal and opposite force on each student *[1 mark]*. As there is no friction, each student will have a resultant force pushing them away from the wall which causes them to move *[1 mark]*.

   b) A *[1 mark]*

The acceleration of each can be found from acceleration = force ÷ mass. The acceleration of student A = 24 ÷ 80 = 0.3 m/s². The acceleration of student B = 24 ÷ 40 = 0.6 m/s², so the difference between the two = 0.6 − 0.3 = 0.3 m/s².

Pages 15-17 — Momentum

1 a) momentum = mass × velocity *[1 mark]*

   b) $p = m \times v = 220 \times 25 =$ **5500 kg m/s**
   [2 marks for correct answer, otherwise 1 mark for correctly substituting in the numbers]

2 Rearrange equation:
   $m = p \div v = 46\ 000 \div 15 = 3066.6... =$ **3070 kg (to 3 s.f.)**
   [3 marks for correct answer, otherwise 1 mark for rearranging the equation, 1 mark for rounding to an appropriate degree of accuracy]

3 In Figure 1, the total momentum of the system is equal to the mass of the moving ball multiplied by its velocity *[1 mark]*. As it hits the line of balls, it transfers this momentum to them and comes to a stop. All of this momentum is transferred along the line of balls to the ball at the end of the line, which is why the middle balls don't move *[1 mark]*. This final ball has the momentum of the first ball, causing it to move with the same velocity (because all of the balls have the same mass) that the moving ball in Figure 1 had *[1 mark]*. In Figure 2, the total momentum of the system is equal to the total momentum in Figure 1 *[1 mark]*.

4 $F = (mv - mu) \div t$, so:
   $mv - mu = Ft$
   $m = Ft \div (v - u) = -0.15 \times 4 \div (0 - 3) =$ **0.2 kg**
   [3 marks for correct answer, otherwise 1 mark for correctly rearranging the equation, 1 mark for substituting in the correct numbers]

5 $p = mv$
   Before collision:
   Momentum of first player = $80 \times 8.0 = 640$ kg m/s
   Momentum of second player = $100 \times -5.5 = -550$ kg m/s
   Total momentum = $640 - 550 = 90$ kg m/s
   After collision:
   Mass = $80 + 100 = 180$ kg
   Momentum = $180 \times v$
   Momentum before = momentum after, so
   $90 = 180 \times v$
   $v = 90 \div 180 =$ **0.5 m/s**
   [4 marks for correct answer, otherwise 1 mark for stating the equation for momentum, 1 mark for correctly calculating the total momentum before the tackle, 1 mark for correctly calculating the combined mass and substituting this into the equation]

6 Newton's third law says that when ball 1 collides with ball 2, an equal but opposite force is exerted on each object. So the force exerted on ball 2 during the collision is 6 N.
   $F = (mv - mu) \div t$
   $(mv - mu) = F \times t$
   $v = (F \times t + mu) \div m$
   $= (6 \times 0.1 + 0.2 \times 0) \div 0.2 =$ **3 m/s**
   [5 marks for correct answer, otherwise 1 mark for correct equation for force, 1 mark for correctly stating the force on ball 2, 1 mark for rearranging the equation for v, 1 mark for correctly substituting the numbers into the equation]

7 a) Trial 6 *[1 mark]*.

   b) E.g. it will be difficult for the student to set vehicle A moving with a consistent speed, so it may take many trials to get another measurement of the same speed *[1 mark]*.

   c) E.g. if the mass of vehicle B gets too large, it may not be held up by the air jets on the air track any more *[1 mark]*. This would cause the vehicle to come into contact with the track, and experience friction, making the results for the speed of vehicle B immediately after the collision less accurate *[1 mark]*.

Also, if the mass of vehicle B gets too big it could also move too slowly to be measured accurately by the light gate. Or it could cause vehicle A to come to a stop before it passes through the gate.

Pages 18-19 — Stopping Distances and Reaction Times

1 a) The distance travelled during the driver's reaction time *[1 mark]*.

   b) Stopping distance = thinking distance + braking distance
   $12 + 24 =$ **36 m** *[1 mark]*

2 a) B *[1 mark]*

   b) Any three from: tiredness / alcohol / drugs / distractions
   [3 marks — 1 mark for each correct answer]

3 a) The distance travelled under the braking force of the vehicle *[1 mark]*.

   b) There will be less friction between the tyres and the road (than there would be if the road was dry and clear of leaves) *[1 mark]*, and so the braking distance will increase *[1 mark]*.

4 a) E.g. clicking a mouse when a computer screen changes colour *[1 mark]*.

   b) Hold a ruler between the open forefinger and thumb of the person being tested *[1 mark]*. Align their finger to the zero line of the ruler *[1 mark]*. Drop the ruler without warning *[1 mark]* and have the test subject close their thumb and finger to catch the ruler *[1 mark]*. The distance the ruler falls can be read from the ruler *[1 mark]*. The time taken for it to fall can be calculated, as the acceleration (due to gravity) is constant. This is the reaction time of the test subject *[1 mark]*.

5 How to grade your answer:
   Level 0: There is no relevant information. *[0 marks]*
   Level 1: There is a brief description of at least one factor that would affect the car's stopping distance, and the effect that it would have. The points made are basic and not linked together. *[1-2 marks]*
   Level 2: There is a more detailed description of some of the factors that would affect the car's stopping distance, and the effect that each factor would have. Some of the points made are linked together. *[3-4 marks]*
   Level 3: There is a clear detailed description of the factors that would affect the car's stopping distance, and an explanation of the effect that each factor would have. The points made are well-linked and the answer has a clear and logical structure. *[5-6 marks]*

   Here are some points your answer may include:
   The driver's reaction time may be increased by being tired. Increasing the driver's reaction time will increase their thinking distance, which will increase the stopping distance.
   The stopping distance may also be increased by the distractions of their friends talking / the music on the radio.
   The car's stopping distance may be increased by the wet weather. This is because the wet weather may increase the car's braking distance.
   The car has a group of people in it, which means its mass is higher than if there was only the driver in the car, and it will take longer to stop.
   The condition of the brakes could affect the stopping distance, as brakes that are worn or faulty are likely to increase the braking distance.
   The speed at which the car is travelling will affect its braking distance.
   A car that's travelling faster will take longer to stop.
   The dark and wet conditions also make the situation less safe as they may mean the driver is less likely to notice a hazard in time to stop.

Page 20 — Stopping Safely

1 a) $KE = \frac{1}{2}mv^2$ and $W = Fd$
$KE = W$, so $\frac{1}{2}mv^2 = Fd$
rearranging gives $d = \dfrac{mv^2}{2F} = \dfrac{1000 \times 12^2}{2 \times 6000} = \mathbf{12\ m}$
[3 marks for a correct answer, otherwise 1 mark for correctly stating the equations for the energy in the car's kinetic energy store and the work done by the brakes, 1 mark for combining and rearranging these equations.]

b) Estimate for reaction time = 0.5 s
thinking distance = 0.5 × 12 = 6 m
stopping distance = thinking distance + braking distance
= 6 + 12 = **18 m**
[2 marks for a correct answer, otherwise 1 mark for correctly calculating the thinking distance]

c) A *[1 mark]*

2 distance = speed × time = 18 × 0.5 = 9 m
So thinking distance is 9 m when travelling at 18 m/s.
So braking distance is 45 − 9 = 36 m.
36 m/s is double 18 m/s. The speed doubles, so the thinking distance doubles:
9 × 2 = 18 m
And as the speed doubles, the braking distance increases four-fold (2^2): 36 × 2^2 = 144 m
Stopping distance = 18 + 144 = **162 m**
[6 marks for correct answer, otherwise 1 mark for stating the equation distance = speed × time, 1 mark for correctly substituting the numbers into this equation, 1 mark for calculating the braking distance, 1 mark for showing that if speed doubles the thinking distance doubles, 1 mark for saying that if the speed doubles the braking distance increases four-fold]

Section 2 — Conservation of Energy

Page 21 — Energy Stores

Warm-up
Kinetic energy store — A toy car rolling along the ground
Magnetic energy store — Two magnets attracted to each other
Electrostatic energy store — Two electric charges repelling each other
Chemical energy store — Petrol in a car
Elastic potential energy store — A stretched rubber band
Nuclear energy store — A nucleus about to undergo a nuclear reaction
Thermal energy store — A hot potato
Gravitational potential energy store — A person on top of a mountain

1 change in gravitational potential energy = mass × gravitational field strength × change in vertical height
= 0.1 × 10 × 0.5 = **0.5 J**
[2 marks for the correct answer, otherwise 1 mark for correctly substituting in the numbers]

2 a) kinetic energy = $\frac{1}{2}$ × mass × (speed)^2 *[1 mark]*

b) ΔGPE = 0.50 × 10 × 42 = 210 J
$\frac{1}{2}mv^2 = 210$
$v^2 = (2 \times 210) \div 0.5 = 840$
$v = \sqrt{840} = 28.98... = \mathbf{29\ m/s\ (to\ 2\ s.f.)}$
[5 marks for the correct answer, otherwise 1 mark for correctly substituting the values into the equation for change in gravitational potential energy, 1 mark for correct value for energy transferred to the kinetic energy store of the rock, 1 mark for correctly rearranging the equation for v or v^2, 1 mark for correctly substituting the numbers into this equation]

Page 22 — Transferring Energy

Warm-up
From left to right: mechanically, by heating

1 a) Energy can be stored, transferred between stores or dissipated — but it can never be created or destroyed *[1 mark]*.

b) Electrically *[1 mark]*.

c) Energy is transferred mechanically *[1 mark]* from the gravitational potential energy store of the bike *[1 mark]* to the kinetic energy store of the bike *[1 mark]*.

d) The golf club has energy in its kinetic energy store *[1 mark]*. Some of this energy is transferred mechanically to the kinetic energy store of the ball *[1 mark]*. Some is transferred mechanically to the thermal energy stores of the golf club and the ball (and to the surroundings by heating) *[1 mark]*. The rest is carried away by sound *[1 mark]*.

Pages 23-24 — Efficiency

1 a) E.g. by heating the fan / by heating the surroundings / transferred away by sound waves
[1 mark for one correct answer]

b) Find the energy that is transferred usefully:
useful energy transferred = total energy input − wasted energy
= 7250 − 2030 = 5220 J
efficiency = $\dfrac{\text{useful energy transferred}}{\text{total energy supplied}} = \dfrac{5220}{7250} = \mathbf{0.72}$ (or **72%**)
[3 marks for correct answer, otherwise 1 mark for calculating the useful energy transferred, 1 mark for correctly stating the efficiency equation]

2 a) Useful energy transferred by air blower:
efficiency = useful energy transferred ÷ total energy supplied
so useful energy transferred by air blower = efficiency × total energy supplied
= 0.6 × 30 000
= 18 000 J
Useful energy transferred by the turbine:
Efficiency = 12% = 0.12
total energy supplied = useful energy transferred by air blower
useful energy transferred by turbine = efficiency × total energy supplied
= 0.12 × 18 000
= **2160 W**
[4 marks for correct answer, otherwise 1 mark for stating the efficiency equation, 1 mark for finding the amount of energy usefully transferred by the air blower, 1 mark for substituting the correct numbers into the efficiency equation to find the useful energy transferred by the turbine]

b) Any two from: e.g. adding more sails so there is a larger surface area for the air to hit / increasing the size of the sails so there is a larger surface area for the air to hit / adding a lubricant to the moving parts of the turbine to reduce friction / changing the angle of the sails so they get hit by more wind / using wires with a lower resistance
[2 marks — 1 mark for each sensible suggestion]

3 a) E.g. the student could measure the temperature of the water in the kettle, so that they can be sure they measure the energy transferred to increase the water's temperature to 100 °C (not any more or less) *[1 mark]*.

b) The student will record an inaccurate value of energy supplied to the kettle for this reading *[1 mark]*. This is because some of the residual energy in the kettle's thermal energy store from the previous trial will be transferred to the water and begin to increase its temperature, so less energy will need to be supplied from the power supply to boil the water *[1 mark]*.

c) The results are not consistent with the prediction.
By calculating the efficiencies at different volumes from the data in Figure 2, using efficiency = $\dfrac{\text{useful energy transferred by device}}{\text{total energy supplied to device}}$
[1 mark], it can be seen that:
E.g. for 660 cm^3 of water, efficiency = 0.168 ÷ 0.212
= 0.792... *[1 mark]*,
while for 2000 cm^3 of water, efficiency = 0.504 ÷ 0.547
= 0.921... *[1 mark]*.
Therefore, the efficiency of the kettle was greater for a larger volume of water than a smaller volume (the opposite of the student's prediction) *[1 mark]*.
You don't have to have done the exact same calculations we have here. As long as you've come to the right conclusion and have done some calculations to show that efficiency is larger for a bigger volume than a smaller volume, you'll get the marks.

Page 25 — Reducing Unwanted Energy Transfers

1 The oil acts as a lubricant *[1 mark]*, which reduces the energy lost due to friction *[1 mark]*.
Instead of saying that the oil acts as a lubricant, you could have said that the oil reduces the amount of friction to gain the first mark here.

2 a) D *[1 mark]*
A low thermal conductivity means the rate of energy transfer through the bricks is lower. A thicker wall will reduce the rate of energy transfer.

b) E.g. the builder could use cavity walls *[1 mark]*.

c) Wasted energy = total energy input − useful energy output
= 22.5 − 13.5 = **9 kJ** *[1 mark]*

140

Pages 26-27 — Energy Resources

Warm-up
Renewable — bio-fuel, solar, tidal, hydro-electricity, wind
Non-renewable — oil, coal, gas, nuclear fuel

1   E.g. a non-renewable energy resource will one day run out *[1 mark]* but a renewable energy resource is renewed as it is used *[1 mark]*.

2 a)   coal, oil, (natural) gas *[1 mark]*

   b)   E.g. burning coal on fires / using gas central heating / generating electricity / using a gas fire
     [1 mark for any correct answer]

   c)   Bio-fuels are solids, liquids or gases that are produced from plants or from animal waste *[1 mark]*.

   d)   E.g. because fossil fuels will eventually run out / because fossil fuels harm the environment
     [1 mark for any correct answer]

3 a)   E.g. wind turbines can be noisy / they spoil the view
     [2 marks — 1 mark for each correct answer]

   b)   E.g. solar panels only produce electricity in the daytime / wind turbines can produce electricity through the night
     [1 mark for any correct answer]

4 a)   E.g. Both energy resources are reliable *[1 mark]*. Both methods of producing electricity have minimal running costs *[1 mark]* and no fuel costs *[1 mark]*. Hydro-electric power plants require the flooding of valleys, which causes a loss of habitat for animals/plants *[1 mark]*. Tidal barrages create no pollution, but they do alter the habitat of nearby animals *[1 mark]*.

   b)   How to grade your answer:
     Level 0:   There is no relevant information. *[0 marks]*
     Level 1:   There is a brief explanation of an advantage or a disadvantage of fossil fuels. The points made are basic and not linked together. *[1-2 marks]*
     Level 2:   There is some explanation of both advantages and disadvantages of fossil fuels. Some of the points made are linked together. *[3-4 marks]*
     Level 3:   There is a clear and detailed explanation of the advantages and disadvantages of using fossil fuels. The points made are well-linked and the answer has a clear and logical structure. *[5-6 marks]*

Here are some points your answer may include:
Advantages:
Fossil fuels are reliable.
They are extracted at a fast enough rate that there is always some in stock.
Power plants can respond quickly to peaks in demand.
Running costs of fossil fuel power plants aren't that expensive compared to other energy resources.
Fuel extraction costs are also low.
Disadvantages:
Fossil fuels are slowly running out / they are a non-renewable energy resource.
Burning fossil fuels releases carbon dioxide into the atmosphere.
Carbon dioxide in the atmosphere contributes to global warming.
Burning coal and oil also releases sulfur dioxide, which causes acid rain.
Oil spillages kill sea life and birds and mammals that live near to the sea.

Page 28 — Trends in Energy Resource Use

1 a)   1.2 TWh *[1 mark]*
   b) i)   2015: 3.0 + 1.6 = 4.6 TWh
     1995: 3.8 + 0.2 = 4.0 TWh
     4.6 − 4.0 = **0.6 TWh**
     [2 marks for a correct answer, otherwise 1 mark for correctly calculating the electricity produced each year.]
    ii)   E.g. the population may have increased / people may have started using electricity for more things *[1 mark]*.

c)   E.g. from 1995 to 2015, the production of electricity from non-renewable sources has decreased from 3.8 to 3 TWh *[1 mark]* and the production of electricity from renewable resources has increased, from 0.2 to 1.2 TWh *[1 mark]*. This may be because the country wants to decrease their use of non-renewable energy sources because they will run out one day/because non-renewables cause a lot of environmental damage *[1 mark]*. The country may want to increase their use of renewable sources because they won't run out /they don't cause as much environmental damage as non-renewable sources *[1 mark]*.

You could have used any data from the graph, as long as it supported the trend you were describing. You could also have given other reasons for the trend, such as becoming increasingly worried about nuclear accidents and nuclear waste, or renewable energy sources having improved in efficiency between 1995 and 2015.

Section 3 — Waves and the Electromagnetic Spectrum

Pages 29-30 — Wave Basics

Warm-up
E.g.

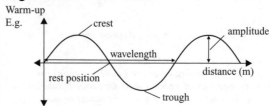

1   C *[1 mark]*
2   B *[1 mark]*
3 a)   E.g. they both transfer energy (or information) but not particles / they both have a wavelength/period/frequency/speed *[1 mark]*.
   b)   In longitudinal waves, the vibrations are parallel to the wave's direction of travel *[1 mark]*, but in transverse waves, the vibrations are at right angles to the wave's direction of travel *[1 mark]*.
4 a)   Because although the ripples travel across the pond, the water just travels up and down, so the ripples cannot move the leaf across the pond *[1 mark]*.
   b)   1.4 ÷ 100 = 0.014 m
     wave speed = frequency × wavelength
             = 15 × 0.014 = **0.21 m/s**
     [2 marks for correct answer, otherwise 1 mark for correct substitution.]
   c)   The time taken for a full cycle of a wave to pass a point *[1 mark]*.
5 a) i)   wave speed = distance ÷ time, or $v = x \div t$ *[1 mark]*
    ii)   time = distance ÷ wave speed = 17 ÷ 340 = **0.05 s**
     [2 marks for correct answer, otherwise 1 mark for correct substitution.]
   b)   Frequency is the number of waves passing a point per second, so 220 × 5 = **1100 waves**
     [2 marks for a correct answer, otherwise 1 mark for multiplying the frequency by the number of seconds.]

Here, you assume that the frequency of the sound waves the violin produces is the same as the frequency of the waves on the violin's strings.

Pages 31-32 — Measuring Waves

1   Rod length = $\lambda \div 2$, so $\lambda = 2 \times 0.2 = 0.4$ m
   $v = f\lambda = 8500 \times 0.4 = $ **3400 m/s**
   [4 marks for correct answer, otherwise 1 mark for correct calculation of wavelength, 1 mark for correct equation, 1 mark for correct substitution]

2 a)   Any two from: e.g. the position of the dipper / the position of the cork when she starts timing / the depth of water in the tank / the equipment used.
     [2 marks — 1 mark for each correct answer]
   b) i)   The result of the third trial is anomalous.
     (12 + 11 + 11 + 14) ÷ 4 = **12**
     [3 marks for correct answer, otherwise 1 mark for identifying the anomalous result, 1 mark for correct method for calculating the average number of bobs]
    ii)   Frequency = number of bobs per second
     12 ÷ 30 = **0.4 Hz**
     [2 marks for a correct answer, otherwise 1 mark for correct calculation.]
   c) i)   wave speed = frequency × wavelength *[1 mark]*

Answers

ii) 10 waves cover 0.18 m
So 1 wavelength = 0.18 ÷ 10 = 0.018 m
$v = 12 \times 0.018 = 0.216 = \textbf{0.22 m/s (to 2 s.f.)}$
[3 marks for correct answer to correct number of significant figures, otherwise 1 mark for correct substitution, 1 mark for correct numerical value for wave speed.]

3   How to grade your answer:
Level 0:   There is no relevant information. *[0 marks]*
Level 1:   A simple method to find the speed of sound waves in air is partly outlined. The points made are basic and not linked together. *[1-2 marks]*
Level 2:   A method to find the speed of sound in air is outlined in some detail. Some of the points made are linked together. *[3-4 marks]*
Level 3:   A method to find the speed of sound waves in air is fully explained in detail. The points made are well-linked and the answer has a clear and logical structure. *[5-6 marks]*

Here are some points your answer may include:
Connect a signal generator to a speaker and set it to generate a sound of a specific frequency.
Connect two microphones to an oscilloscope so that the waves detected at each microphone will be displayed as separate waveforms on the oscilloscope.
Place the microphones next to each other in front of the speaker.
At this point, the waveforms will be aligned with each other on the oscilloscope (i.e. peaks and troughs appear at the same point).
Keeping both microphones directly in front of the speaker, slowly move one microphone away from the speaker, until the two wave-forms on the oscilloscope next become aligned.
The microphones should now be located one wavelength of the sound apart.
Measure this distance, λ, and note down the frequency of the sound generated, f.
Use the formula $v = f\lambda$ to calculate the speed of sound, v.
To get more accurate results the experiment can be repeated for different frequencies and a mean value calculated.

Pages 33-34 — Wave Behaviour at Boundaries

Warm-up
wave is reflected — it bounces back off the material
wave is absorbed — it transfers all its energy to the material
wave is transmitted — it passes through the material

1 a)   E.g. an echo would be created *[1 mark]*
   b)   E.g. the black object would heat up *[1 mark]*
2 a)   30° *[1 mark]*
   b)

[1 mark for straight refracted ray bending towards the normal, 1 mark for correct angle of refraction]

3 a)   Glass is (optically) denser than air *[1 mark]* because the refracted ray bends towards the normal *[1 mark]*.
   b)   As the light ray enters the glass block, it slows down *[1 mark]*. The frequency of the ray remains the same *[1 mark]* and its wavelength decreases (because $v = f\lambda$ and v has decreased) *[1 mark]*.
4   White light is made up of different wavelengths of light, which we see as different colours *[1 mark]*. When these different wavelengths enter the block, they refract by different amounts *[1 mark]*, as shorter wavelengths of light refract more than longer ones at the same boundary. This means the colours in the white light separate slightly and the colours on the edges of the spectrum (red and purple) can be seen *[1 mark]*.

Page 35 — Sound

1   E.g. size of the eardrum, shape of the eardrum
      [2 marks — 1 mark for each correct answer]
2   A *[1 mark]*
3   A child speaks and produces sound wave. The particles in the air vibrate back and forth (creating compressions and rarefactions) as the sound wave travels through the air to the end of the pot *[1 mark]*. When the sound wave hits the pot, the air particles hitting the base of the pot cause it to move back and forth (vibrate) *[1 mark]*. This causes particles in the end of the string tied to the pot to vibrate *[1 mark]*. The particles in the string vibrate and transmit the wave along the string *[1 mark]*. When the vibrations reach the other end of the string, they are transmitted to the base of the second pot. This causes the surrounding air particles to vibrate, generating a sound wave which is heard by the second child *[1 mark]*.

Page 36 — Ultrasound

1   D *[1 mark]*
2   Pulses of ultrasound are directed towards the foetus *[1 mark]*. They are partially reflected at each boundary, e.g. the lining of the womb and the boundary between the fluid in the womb and the foetus *[1 mark]*. The reflections are detected and their timings and distributions are used to produce a video image of inside the womb *[1 mark]*.
3 a)   The time between sending and detecting the pulse is the time it takes for the pulse to travel to an object and back again
      So to find the distance to the object reflecting the waves, halve the time: $1.05 \div 2 = 0.525$ s
      distance = wave speed × time = $1520 \times 0.525 = 798$ m
      This suggests that there may be a submarine under the ship, as the ultrasound wave was reflected by something about halfway between the ship and the seabed.
      [3 marks for a correct answer, with a correct supporting calculation, otherwise 1 mark for a correctly calculated distance, 1 mark for a correct answer supporting statement based on the calculation.]
   b)   E.g. they could be coated with something that absorbed ultrasound waves (e.g. rubber). This would mean that fewer/no waves were reflected, so it would be harder for a boat to find the submarine. / They could stay close to the sea bed. This would mean that waves would take roughly the same amount of time to be reflected from the submarine as the sea bed, so the submarine would be harder to detect. *[1 mark for a sensible suggestion, and 1 mark for a logical supporting explanation.]*

Page 37 — Infrasound and Seismic Waves

1 a)   Sound waves below 20 Hz *[1 mark]*.
   b)   E.g. tracking animals / monitoring volcanoes *[1 mark]*
2 a)   As there are no S-waves at C, something is stopping them *[1 mark]*. S-waves cannot pass through a liquid so it is likely that part of the interior of the Earth is in a liquid state *[1 mark]*.
   b)   At both points the waves pass between a solid and a liquid medium *[1 mark]*. They travel at different speeds in solids and liquids, so they experience a sudden change in velocity *[1 mark]*.

Pages 38-39 — Reflection

1 a)   The angle of incidence always equals the angle of reflection *[1 mark]*.
   b)   E.g. total internal reflection is where a wave travelling through a material hits a boundary and is completely reflected back into the first material *[1 mark]*. For this to occur, the angle of incidence must be greater than the critical angle of the material *[1 mark]* and the second material must be less optically dense than the first *[1 mark]*.
2

[1 mark for normal lines drawn correctly, 1 mark for drawing both reflected light rays correctly]

3 a)   specular reflection *[1 mark]*
   b)   The rough surface means that the angle of incidence is different for each ray across the width of the beam *[1 mark]*. This means each ray is reflected in a different direction, so the light is scattered *[1 mark]*.
4 a)   E.g. as the beam is narrower than the distance between the markers on the protractor's scale, it will be easier to measure angles to the nearest degree *[1 mark]*, so it is less likely that there will be human errors (due to judgement) in the results *[1 mark]*. This means their results will be more accurate *[1 mark]*.

Answers

142

b) i) E.g.

[1 mark for correctly labelled axes with a sensible scale, 1 mark for all points plotted correctly, 1 mark for a straight line of best fit that passes through or close to all the points]

ii) The graph shows it does not agree with the law of reflection because e.g. the data/line of best fit does not fall along the line angle of incidence = angle of reflection *[1 mark]*

iii) E.g. the normal not being drawn perpendicular/at 90 °C to the mirror *[1 mark]*.

Page 40 — *Investigating Refraction*

1 a) E.g. A ray box creates a thin ray of light which is easy to trace *[1 mark]*

b)

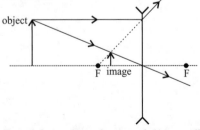

[1 mark for a correctly completed diagram]

c) 18° *[1 mark]* (Allow between 17° and 19°)

d) Water *[1 mark]* as it has the largest angle of refraction *[1 mark]* which means it has bent the ray the least and so the change of speed of the ray is the smallest *[1 mark]*.

Page 41 — *Visible Light and Colour*

1 B *[1 mark]*.

2 a) red *[1 mark]*

b) Black *[1 mark]*. The red filter absorbs all colours of light except for red, so only red light reaches the cube *[1 mark]*. The blue cube absorbs all wavelengths of light apart from blue, so it absorbs all of the light that reaches it, making it appear black *[1 mark]*.

c) No light would be able to escape from the ray box *[1 mark]*.

Pages 42-43 — *Lenses and Ray Diagrams*

Warm-up

Usually called a diverging lens.

Also known as a concave lens.

Spreads parallel rays out.

Usually called a converging lens.

Also known as a convex lens.

Brings parallel rays together to a point.

1 a) The surface of lens 1 would be more curved *[1 mark]*

b) An image created at the point where rays of light are brought together *[1 mark]*.

c) C *[1 mark]*

2

[1 mark for ray drawn from top of object parallel to axis, diverging at the lens, 1 mark for tracing the refracted ray back to the principal focus, 1 mark for a ray drawn from the top of the object straight through the centre of the lens, 1 mark for image drawn at the point where the rays meet.]

3 a) E.g.

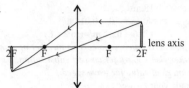

lens axis

[1 mark for an inverted image at 2F on the left hand side of the lens, 1 mark for an image the same size as the object, 1 mark for a ray drawn passing from the top of the object to the top of the image, through the centre of the lens, without refracting, 1 mark for a ray drawn from the top of the object parallel to the lens axis, refracting at the lens, and joining the first ray at the top of the image.]

You could also draw a line from the top of the object straight through the focal length, which will then be parallel to the axis after it reaches the lens.

b) The image will move to be on the same side of the lens as the object, further from the lens than the object *[1 mark]*. The image will be bigger *[1 mark]* and will be the right way up *[1 mark]*.

Pages 44-45 — *Electromagnetic Waves*

Warm-up

True, True, False

1 a) From left to right: Infrared *[1 mark]*, X-rays. *[1 mark]*

b) Arrow must point to the left (i.e. from gamma rays to radio waves / from high energy to low energy) *[1 mark]*.

c) From left to right: yellow, green, blue, indigo *[2 marks for all correct, 1 mark for 3 correct]*

d) The nucleus *[1 mark]*

2 a) As the frequency increases, so does the potential danger *[1 mark]*.

b) Infrared — skin burns
Microwaves — internal heating of cells
X-rays — cell mutation and cancer
[1 mark for all 3 correct]

c) Any two from: e.g. damage to surface cells of skin/skin cancer *[1 mark]* / damage to surface cells of eyes/eye conditions *[1 mark]*

3 a) i) Source: X-ray machine
Observer: Photographic film/Radiation badge
[1 mark for two sensible answers]

ii) Energy is transferred from the kinetic energy store of the electrons *[1 mark]* by radiation (the X-rays) to the chemical energy store of the photographic film *[1 mark]*.

b) E.g. infrared waves transferring energy from a heater's thermal energy store to the thermal energy store of a person *[1 mark]*.

Pages 46-48 — *Emitting and Absorbing EM Radiation*

Warm-up

Most objects emit radiation across a <u>broad</u> range of wavelengths.
The intensity and <u>distribution</u> of these wavelengths depends on the object's <u>temperature</u>.

1 a) It remains constant *[1 mark]*.

b) The average power radiated by the object is more than the average power absorbed by the object *[1 mark]*

2 a) $(62 + 64 + 64) \div 3 = 63.33...$
So the average = **63 °C (to 2 s.f.)**
[2 marks for correct answer, otherwise 1 mark for correct method for calculating the average temperature]

b) Test tube A *[1 mark]* because uncertainty in a mean is range ÷ 2, and the repeated results for Test tube A have the biggest range (equal to 68 − 65 = 3). *[1 mark]*

c) Any one from: e.g. take more frequent measurements of temperature / for each repeat, measure the temperature every thirty seconds for three minutes / use a digital thermometer *[1 mark for any sensible suggestion]*

3 How to grade your answer:

Level 0: There is no relevant information. *[0 marks]*

Level 1: There is a brief explanation of how the Earth absorbs radiation emitted by the Sun. The points made are basic and not linked together. *[1-2 marks]*

Level 2: There is an explanation of how the Earth emits radiation and absorbs radiation emitted by the Sun and how this affects the Earth's temperature at different times of the day. Some of the points made are linked together. *[3-4 marks]*

Level 3: There is a detailed explanation of how the Earth emits radiation and reflects or absorbs radiation emitted by the Sun and how the balance between these at different times of the day keeps the Earth's temperature constant. The points made are well-linked and the answer has a clear and logical structure. *[5-6 marks]*
Here are some points your answer may include:
During the day, the half of the Earth which is facing the Sun is hit by radiation emitted by the Sun.
Some of this radiation is reflected by Earth's atmosphere, clouds and the Earth's surface.
Most is absorbed by the atmosphere, clouds and the Earth's surface.
Radiation is also emitted from the atmosphere/clouds/Earth's surface.
During the day, the amount of radiation absorbed is greater than the amount that is reflected or emitted.
This causes an increase in local temperature.
The half of the Earth which is facing away from the Sun has no radiation from the Sun hitting it — it is night time.
This half of the Earth absorbs and reflects very little radiation, but emits radiation at its usual rate.
So at night time more radiation is being emitted than is being absorbed.
This causes a decrease in local temperature.
Throughout each full cycle of day and night, one half of the Earth will be increasing in temperature and the other half will be decreasing in temperature.
Overall, these local temperature changes balance out, and so the average temperature of the Earth remains roughly constant.

4 a) E.g.

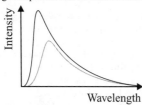

Wavelength

[1 mark for drawing the curve for star C with a peak further to the left than the peak for star A, 1 mark for making the peak higher than the peak for star A.]

b) Star B *[1 mark]*. Its peak wavelength is longer than the peak wavelengths of stars C and A *[1 mark]*, and red light has the longest wavelength of visible light *[1 mark]*.

5 a) Any three from: e.g using the same mass of water in each can / using the same equipment for each can / starting measurements at the same temperature for each can / using cans that are the same size and shape / using cans that are made from the same material *[3 marks]*.

Each of these make sure that the rate of change of temperature is only affected by the paint on the can, not any other properties of the cans, the water, or the experimental set-up. This ensures that it is a fair test, and so the experiment will produce valid results.

b) E.g. the water in can A / the can painted with matt navy blue paint will cool fastest *[1 mark]*. This is because dark and matt surfaces are better emitters of infrared radiation than light and shiny/glossy surfaces *[1 mark]*.

c) E.g.

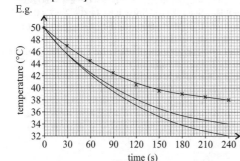

[1 mark for all points drawn correctly, and 1 mark for a smooth curve of best fit which passes through or close to all the points]

Pages 49-52 — Uses of EM Waves

Warm-up
True, True, False, True.

1 a) Ultraviolet — fluorescent lights
Visible light — photography
Infrared — security lights
Radio waves — satellite communications
[2 marks for all four correct, 1 mark for 3 correct]

b) Any two from: e.g. TV remotes / optical fibres / sending files between phones and laptops
[2 marks — 1 mark for each correct answer]

c) B *[1 mark]*

2 a) C *[1 mark]*

b) A UV light can be shone onto the stolen object which will cause the ink to glow/become visible *[1 mark]* and can be used to prove the object belongs to him *[1 mark]*.

c) E.g. marking bank notes *[1 mark]*

3 a) X-rays are directed at the body part being imaged. A detector is placed behind the body. The X-rays are absorbed by bones *[1 mark]*, but transmitted by the rest of the body tissue/muscles *[1 mark]*. A negative image is formed with brighter areas where fewer X-rays get through, indicating the bones *[1 mark]*.

b) E.g. security scans at airports *[1 mark]*

4 a) It detects infrared radiation emitted by an object and converts this into an electrical signal which is displayed on a screen as an image *[1 mark]*. Different temperatures appear brighter/as different colours, so you can build a thermal image of the surroundings *[1 mark]*.

b) When it is dark there is very little visible light for a normal camera to pick up so a hiding criminal could be hard to see *[1 mark]*. The criminal will be warmer than the surroundings and so will emit more infrared radiation *[1 mark]*. This will make them stand out from the surroundings if using an infrared camera *[1 mark]*.

5 a) The microwaves are absorbed by water molecules in the potato *[1 mark]*. This transfers energy to the water molecules, causing the water in the potato to heat up *[1 mark]*. The water molecules transfer the energy they have absorbed to the rest of the molecules in the potato (by conduction), cooking it *[1 mark]*.

b) The glass plate does not absorb any microwaves *[1 mark]* as it does not contain any water molecules, and so it is only heated by (conduction from) the potato *[1 mark]*.

6 a) An alternating current (a current made of oscillating charges) flows through walkie-talkie *[1 mark]*. Electrons in the walkie-talkie's aerial oscillate, producing radio waves *[1 mark]*. These radio waves travel through the air to the aerial of the second walkie-talkie, where they are absorbed *[1 mark]*. The energy carried by the radio waves is transferred to the electrons in the receiver aerial *[1 mark]*. This causes electrons in the aerial to oscillate *[1 mark]* which produces an alternating current in the second walkie-talkie *[1 mark]*.

b) How to grade your answer:
Level 0: There is no relevant information. *[0 marks]*
Level 1: There is a brief explanation of the differences between radio wave types used for broadcasting.
The points made are basic and not linked together. *[1-2 marks]*
Level 2: There is some explanation of the differences between radio wave types used for broadcasting, including their different ranges and how this affects which broadcast can be heard. Some of the points made are linked together. *[3-4 marks]*
Level 3: There is a clear and detailed explanation of the differences between radio wave types used for broadcasting, including their different ranges and how this affects which broadcast can be heard. The points made are well-linked and the answer has a clear and logical structure. *[5-6 marks]*
Here are some points your answer may include:
FM radio is transmitted using very short wavelength radio waves.
These radio waves can only be received while the receiver is in direct sight of the transmitter.
This is because these wavelengths are easily absorbed by obstacles, e.g. buildings, and cannot bend much around obstacles.
France is far away, so the signal cannot be received in France.
Long-wave radio waves can be transmitted over long distances.
This is because long-wave radio waves bend around the curved surface of the Earth.
Long-wave radio waves can also bend around obstacles such as mountains.
Hence the signal can travel a long distance and be received in France.

Section 4 — Radioactivity

Page 53 — The Model of the Atom

Warm-up

1×10^{-10} m

1 a) The plum pudding model *[1 mark]*. This model describes an atom as a sphere of positive charge, with electrons spread throughout it *[1 mark]*.

b) E.g.:
Property: The atom is mostly made up of empty space / most of the atom's mass is concentrated at the centre in a tiny nucleus *[1 mark]*. Observation: Most of the alpha particles they fired at the thin gold foil passed straight through *[1 mark]*.

2 a) Proton: (+)1 *[1 mark]*
Neutron: 0 *[1 mark]*

b) The protons and neutrons make up a central nucleus *[1 mark]* and the electrons orbit the nucleus *[1 mark]*.

c) 26 electrons *[1 mark]*. Protons and electrons have equal but opposite charges (and neutrons are neutral). As there are the same number of protons and neutrons in an atom, atoms are neutral *[1 mark]*.

Page 54 — Electron Energy Levels

Warm-up

In Bohr's atomic model, electrons orbit <u>the nucleus</u> at <u>fixed</u> distances called energy levels or <u>shells</u>.

1 a) An electron can move into a higher energy level / further from the nucleus, by absorbing electromagnetic radiation *[1 mark]*, and move into a lower energy level / closer to the nucleus, by emitting electromagnetic radiation *[1 mark]*.

b) Ion *[1 mark]*

c) +1 *[1 mark]*

2 As you get further away from a nucleus, the energy levels get closer together *[1 mark]*. So electrons falling to the first energy level have a greater change in energy than those falling to the second energy level *[1 mark]*. This means they release electromagnetic radiation with a higher energy *[1 mark]* and so a higher frequency is released when an electron falls to the first energy level *[1 mark]*.

Pages 55-57 — Isotopes and Nuclear Radiation

Warm-up

A — mass number, Z — atomic number, X — element symbol

1 a) Atoms with the same number of protons *[1 mark]* but different numbers of neutrons (in their nucleus) *[1 mark]*.

b) alpha, beta, gamma
[3 marks in total — 1 mark for each correct answer]

c) i) alpha *[1 mark]*
ii) E.g. a few centimetres *[1 mark]* because alpha particles are strongly ionising *[1 mark]*.

2 a) beta *[1 mark]*

b) Gamma *[1 mark]* because it is highly penetrating so it can travel through paper and aluminium *[1 mark]*. It can be absorbed by sheets of lead *[1 mark]*.

3 a) 23 *[1 mark]*
Remember that the nucleon number is another name for the mass number.

b) 23 − 11 = 12 neutrons *[1 mark]*
The number of neutrons is the difference between the mass number and the atomic number.

c) D *[1 mark]*
An isotope has the same number of protons (so the same atomic number), but a different number of neutrons (so a different mass number).

d) The atomic number of the neon isotope is lower, so there are fewer protons in the neon isotope's nucleus *[1 mark]*. So the charge on the neon isotope's nucleus is lower than the charge on the sodium isotope's nucleus *[1 mark]*.

4 a) For 0.5 mm thickness:
uncertainty = range ÷ 2 = (122 − 99) ÷ 2 = **11.5** *[1 mark]*
For 0.6 mm thickness:
mean = (93 + 95 + 98) ÷ 3
= 95.33... = **95 (to nearest whole number)** *[1 mark]*

b) The results for a thickness of 0.6 mm are the most precise, as they have the smallest range / they have the smallest uncertainty / the individual results are closest to the mean value for count-rate *[1 mark]*. It's not possible to know whether they are the most accurate, as you can't tell from the data how close to the true value the measurements are *[1 mark]*.

c) E.g. the thicker the paper, the less beta radiation reaches the detector / the more beta radiation is absorbed by the paper *[1 mark]*.

d) If the half-life was shorter than or close to the duration of the

experiment, the count-rate would reduce significantly during the experiment *[1 mark]*, and it would not be possible to conclude if a decrease in count-rate was due to the paper or the decay of the substance *[1 mark]*.

Page 58 — Nuclear Equations

Warm-up

The atomic number <u>decreases</u> by <u>two</u>.
The mass number <u>decreases</u> by <u>two</u>.

1 a) It increases the positive charge on the nucleus / makes the nucleus 'more positive' *[1 mark]*.

b) No effect *[1 mark]*

2 a) The atomic numbers on each side are not equal *[1 mark]*.

b) $^{0}_{-1}$e or $^{0}_{-1}\beta$ *[1 mark]*
The other particle must be a beta-minus particle, as this will balance the equation.

c) $^{226}_{88}$Ra $\longrightarrow$ $^{222}_{86}$Rn + $^{4}_{2}$He
[3 marks in total — 1 mark for each correct nucleus or particle in standard notation]

You know that the mass number of the radium is 226 (that's what 'radium-226' means). You also know that an alpha particle is $^{4}_{2}$He, so you can find the mass and atomic numbers of radon by balancing the equation.

d) Rn-222 has 222 − 86 = 136 neutrons *[1 mark]*
2 alpha decays = 2 × 2 = 4 neutrons released *[1 mark]*
136 − 4 = **132** *[1 mark]*

Pages 59-60 — Half-life

1 a) E.g. the average time taken for the number of radioactive nuclei in an isotope to halve *[1 mark]*.

b) 75 s *[1 mark]*
You need to find the time it takes for the count rate to halve. For example, the initial count-rate is 60 cps. Half of this is 30 cps, which corresponds to 75 seconds on the time axis.

c) After 1 half-life, there will be 800 ÷ 2 = 400 undecayed nuclei remaining. After 2 half-lives, there will be 400 ÷ 2 = 200 undecayed nuclei remaining.
So 800 − 200 = **600** nuclei will have decayed.
[2 marks for correct answer, otherwise 1 mark for correctly calculating the number of decayed/undecayed nuclei after one half-life]

d) C *[1 mark]*
After 2 half-lives, there are 200 undecayed nuclei. The ratio is 200:800, which simplifies to 1:4. You don't even need the numbers to work out this ratio. For any radioactive isotope, after two half lives, the initial number of undecayed nuclei will have halved and then halved again. It will be one quarter of the original number, so the ratio is always 1:4.

2 a) Isotope 1 (it has the shortest half-life) *[1 mark]*.

b) Isotope 1 *[1 mark]*, because each isotope starts with the same number of nuclei, but isotope 1 has the shortest half-life, so more nuclei will decay per second *[1 mark]*.
For isotope 1, it takes 4 minutes for 10 000 nuclei to decay, but it takes 72 years for 10 000 nuclei of isotope 2 to decay and 5 years for 10 000 nuclei of isotope 3 to decay. The activity of isotope 1 quickly decreases, but it takes longer for isotope 2 and isotope 3's activity to decrease.

3 a) E.g.
After 1 half-life, the activity will be 8800 ÷ 2 = 4400 Bq.
After 2 half-lives, the activity will be 4400 ÷ 2 = 2200 Bq.
After 3 half-lives, the activity will be 2200 ÷ 2 = 1100 Bq.
So it will take **3 half-lives**.
[3 marks for correct answer, otherwise 1 mark for correct method, 1 mark for correct calculations]

b) 6 hours is the same as 3 half-lives
which means that 1 half-life is
6 hours ÷ 3 = **2 hours** *[1 mark]*.

4 a)
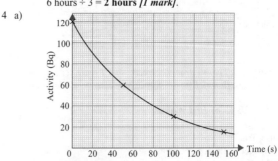
[1 mark for all points plotted correctly, 1 mark for smooth curve joining the points]
Start the graph at 120 Bq. After 50 s, this will have halved to 60 Bq. After another 50 s (i.e. 100 s altogether), it will have halved again, to 30 Bq. Plot these points, then join them up with a nice smooth curve.

b) 70 Bq (accept between 68 Bq and 72 Bq)
[1 mark for correct value from your graph]

c) From a), you know that the activity has dropped to 15 Bq in the first 150 s. 200 s is one more half-life after this.
After 200 s, 15 ÷ 2 = 7.5 = **8 Bq**
[2 marks — 1 mark for correct calculation of activity, 1 mark for correct activity to one significant figure]
E.g. radioactive decay is random *[1 mark]* and the effect of randomness on the results will be greater for lower activities *[1 mark]*.

Pages 61-62 — Background Radiation and Contamination

1 Any two from: e.g. rocks / space/cosmic rays / fallout from nuclear weapons
[2 marks — 1 mark for each correct answer]

2 a) Contamination is when unwanted radioactive particles get onto an object *[1 mark]*. Irradiation is when an object is exposed to radiation *[1 mark]*.

b) For irradiation: e.g. use shielding/stand behind barriers / work in a different room to the source / store the sample in a lead-lined box
For contamination: e.g. wear gloves / handle the source with tongs / wear a protective suit or mask
[2 marks in total — 1 mark for a correct measure for irradiation, 1 mark for a correct measure for contamination]

3 How to grade your answer:
Level 0: There is no relevant information. *[0 marks]*
Level 1: There is a brief explanation of the dangers of contamination or radiation. The points made are basic and not linked together. *[1-2 marks]*
Level 2: There is some explanation of the dangers and risks of contamination and radiation and a conclusion is given with some logical justification. Some of the points made are linked together. *[3-4 marks]*
Level 3: There is a clear and detailed explanation of the dangers and risks of contamination and radiation, used to justify the conclusion that the clockmaker should either be more concerned about contamination or irradiation. The points made are well-linked and the answer has a clear and logical structure. *[5-6 marks]*

Here are some points your answer may include:
Alpha particles are stopped by skin or thin paper.
Being irradiated won't make the clockmaker radioactive.
But irradiation may do some damage to his skin.
However, the radiation cannot penetrate his body and cause damage to his tissue or organs.
If the clockmaker's hands get contaminated with radium-226, he will be exposed to more alpha particles. Or he may accidentally ingest (eat) some.
Or if particles of the radium get into the air, he could breathe them in.
The radium will then decay whilst inside his body.
Alpha particles are strongly ionising.
This means that the alpha particles can do lots of damage to nearby tissue or organs.
So he should be more concerned about contamination.

4 a) E.g. the student's radioactive source could contribute to the count-rate recorded, but would not be present during the scientist's experiment, causing an overestimate in the background count-rate *[1 mark]*.

b) First, find the mean counts in 5 minutes.
Mean counts = (598 + 641 + 624) ÷ 3 *[1 mark]*
= 621 *[1 mark]*
To get count-rate in cps, divide by the number of seconds in 5 minutes.
mean count-rate = 621 ÷ (5 × 60) = **2.07 cps** *[1 mark]*
Alternatively, you could add the three counts together and divide by the number of seconds in fifteen minutes — i.e. combining the steps.

c) i) E.g. put the radioactive substance back into its storage case while replacing the Geiger-Muller tube / place a shielding barrier around the radioactive substance while replacing the Geiger-Muller tube *[1 mark]*.

ii) The scientist's results will be less valid, as changing the distance may change the count-rate detected / the distance between the substance and the Geiger-Muller tube was a control variable in the experiment *[1 mark]*, so the results won't be valid as a measure of only how the count-rate varies with time, and cannot be used to accurately calculate the half-life *[1 mark]*.

Pages 63-64 — Uses of Radiation

Warm-up
Positron-emitting isotopes are attached to substances that are used by the body. These substances are then either swallowed by or injected into the patient and act as a tracer. Positrons are emitted and annihilate with electrons in the nearby tissue. Gamma radiation is emitted, which can be detected outside the body. The amount of radiation detected matches the metabolic activity of the cells in that area, which can be used to determine if the nearby tissue is cancerous.

1 a) Gamma radiation — detecting leaks in underground pipes
Beta radiation — thickness control for paper
Alpha radiation — smoke alarms
[2 mark for all three correct, otherwise 1 mark for one correct]

b) E.g. using radiation means that plastic equipment isn't exposed to high temperatures which could damage or melt it *[1 mark]*.

c) The isotopes have short half-lives *[1 mark]*, so if the source had to travel a long distance, its activity would drop to a low level that would mean it couldn't be used for a PET scan *[1 mark]*.

2 a) Technetium-99m would be injected into the patient, where it would bind to any calcium *[1 mark]*. The technetium would then decay, emitting gamma radiation that could be detected outside the body *[1 mark]*. If there is calcium present within the heart/if the heart tissue is damaged, lots of radiation will be emitted from the heart *[1 mark]*.

b) Because alpha radiation is highly ionising and so would cause damage inside the body *[1 mark]*. It would not be detectable outside the body, as it hasn't got a long range/it cannot penetrate body tissue *[1 mark]*.

3 a) Beta radiation *[1 mark]* as it is ionising enough to pass through the casing of the implant and kill the cells of the tumour, but will also have a short enough range that damage to healthy cells is limited *[1 mark]*.

b) Gamma radiation is used for external radiotherapy *[1 mark]*. Gamma radiation is able to pass through the body and get to delicate organs, which is why the patient and nurses need to be protected *[1 mark]*. The gamma radiation is carefully focussed on the tumour, to reduce damage to healthy cells *[1 mark]* and sometimes shielding is placed on other parts of the body *[1 mark]*. The radiotherapy machines are kept in rooms that are specially shielded, to protect other patients and staff in the hospital *[1 mark]*.

Pages 65-66 — Nuclear Fission and Fusion

Warm-up
It releases energy. Both
It can start when a nucleus absorbs a neutron. Fission
It usually involves large and unstable nuclei. Fission
It usually involves light nuclei. Fusion
Uranium-235 nuclei commonly undergo this. Fission

1 a) Nuclear fusion is when two light nuclei join/fuse together to create a larger nucleus *[1 mark]*.

b) B *[1 mark]*
The energy released from nuclear fusion is due to a difference in the mass of the nuclei before (greater) and after (smaller).

2 a) A nucleus absorbs a slow-moving neutron, which makes it more unstable *[1 mark]*. The unstable nucleus undergoes fission — it splits into two lighter elements (daughter nuclei) *[1 mark]*. Energy is also released, along with two or three neutrons *[1 mark]*. These neutrons can be absorbed by other nuclei, causing more fission (a chain reaction) *[1 mark]*.

b) Neutrons can only be absorbed (to cause fission) if they are slow-moving, thermal neutrons *[1 mark]*. The moderator slows down the neutrons until they have thermal energies and can be absorbed *[1 mark]*. Control rods are used to control the speed of the chain reaction *[1 mark]*. They absorb some neutrons so that there is a steady rate of fission — the products of one fission decay create one new fission decay *[1 mark]*.

3 How to grade your answer:
Level 0: There is no relevant information. *[0 marks]*
Level 1: There is a brief explanation of an advantage or a disadvantage of nuclear power. The points made are basic and not linked together. *[1-2 marks]*
Level 2: There is some explanation of both the advantages and disadvantages of nuclear power. Some of the points made are linked together. *[3-4 marks]*
Level 3: There is a clear and detailed explanation of multiple advantages and disadvantages of nuclear power. The points made are well-linked and the answer has a clear and logical structure. *[5-6 marks]*

Answers

Here are some points your answer may include:

Advantages:

It is a pretty safe method for generating electricity.

It can generate lots of energy from a small amount of fuel compared to other energy resources.

Nuclear fuel is cheap and readily available.

Nuclear power doesn't produce carbon dioxide, which contributes to global warming.

Disadvantages:

Some nuclear waste has a very long half-life so it's hard to dispose of.

The overall cost of a nuclear power plant is high.

There is a small risk of a major catastrophe like Fukoshima.

4   For fusion to occur, two nuclei need to collide and fuse together *[1 mark]*. All nuclei have a positive charge, so there is electrostatic repulsion between them *[1 mark]*. High temperatures and pressures are needed to overcome this and bring the nuclei close enough together that they fuse *[1 mark]*. Lots of energy is needed to create these conditions — more than is released by fusion *[1 mark]*.

Section 5 — Astronomy

Page 67 — The Solar System and Gravity

Warm-up

1. Mercury, 4. Mars, 5. Jupiter, 6. Saturn, 8. Neptune

1 a)   Moon — Planet — Approximately circular
        Comet — Sun — Highly elliptical
        [4 marks in total — 1 mark for each correct answer]

   b)   Any three from: e.g. planets / dwarf planets / asteroids / natural satellites
        [3 marks in total — 1 mark for each correct object]

   c)   Gravitational force *[1 mark]*

2   It would be faster *[1 mark]*. The closer you get to the Sun, the stronger its gravitational field is, so the larger the force acting on the planet *[1 mark]*. This means a larger instantaneous velocity is needed for the planet to be in a stable orbit *[1 mark]*.

Page 68 — Changing Ideas about the Universe

1 a)   Geocentric model *[1 mark]*

   b)   The heliocentric model *[1 mark]*. The planets (including Earth) orbit the Sun *[1 mark]* in elliptical/roughly circular orbits *[1 mark]*.

2 a)   C *[1 mark]*

   b)   All the matter in the Universe was in a small space *[1 mark]*. This space was very hot and dense *[1 mark]*. This space then 'exploded' and began expanding *[1 mark]*.

   c)   The Big Bang theory *[1 mark]*

Page 69 — Red-shift and CMB Radiation

1 a) i)   There is an observed increase in the wavelength of the light from distant galaxies *[1 mark]*, so the light is shifted towards the red end of the electromagnetic spectrum *[1 mark]*.

     ii)   The Sunflower Galaxy *[1 mark]*. It is the most distant galaxy, so it is moving away from us the fastest *[1 mark]*. The faster a galaxy is moving away from us, the more red-shifted the light from it is *[1 mark]*.

    iii)   Measurements of red-shift show all the distant galaxies, (whichever direction you look in) are moving away from us *[1 mark]*. The more distant a galaxy is, the faster it's moving away, which shows the universe is expanding *[1 mark]*. This expansion started from a single point, which is the point at which the Big Bang is said to have originated from *[1 mark]*.

   b)   E.g. the Cosmic Microwave Background radiation (CMB radiation) *[1 mark]*

Page 70 — The Life Cycle of Stars

1 a)   B *[1 mark]*

   b)   A cloud of dust and gas *[1 mark]*

   c)   Gravitational force *[1 mark]*

2 a)   Because the gravitational collapse of the star *[1 mark]* and the thermal expansion outwards due to nuclear fusion *[1 mark]* are in equilibrium *[1 mark]*.

   b)   When a star with a mass much greater than the Sun stops being a red supergiant, it expands and contracts several times until it finally explodes in a supernova *[1 mark]*. This leaves behind a very dense core, called a neutron star *[1 mark]* or, if the star was massive enough, a black hole *[1 mark]*.

Page 71 — Looking into Space

Warm-up

Radio telescope

1 a)   The diameter of the objective lens *[1 mark]*.

   b)   Earth's atmosphere absorbs light from space *[1 mark]*, so placing the telescope in a higher location reduces the amount of atmosphere between the telescope and the distant object and improves the image he can see *[1 mark]*. Light pollution from nearby sources of light makes it hard to see dim objects in the sky *[1 mark]*, so moving the telescope to a darker place will improve the image he can see *[1 mark]*.

2   E.g. optical telescopes detect visible light, but after the 1940s, telescopes were built to detect a range of electromagnetic radiation *[1 mark]*, which allows other parts of the Universe to be seen *[1 mark]*. Using telescopes alongside computers creates clearer and sharper images *[1 mark]* and allows astronomers to capture pictures and store lots of data, making it quicker and easier to analyse *[1 mark]*.

Section 6 — Forces and Energy

Page 72 — Energy Transfers and Systems

1   C *[1 mark]*

2   E.g.

[1 mark for energy transferred electrically from battery, 1 mark for thermal energy store of bulb, 1 mark for energy transfer by radiation or heating from bulb]

3 a) i) $KE = \frac{1}{2}mv^2 = 0.5 \times 0.08 \times 7.00^2 = \mathbf{1.96\ J}$
        [3 marks for correct answer, otherwise 1 mark for correct equation, 1 mark for correct substitution]

     ii)   Work done by gravitational force *[1 mark]*

   b) $\Delta GPE = mg\Delta h = 1.96$
        $\Delta h = 1.96 \div mg = 1.96 \div (0.08 \times 10) = \mathbf{2.45\ m}$
        [4 marks for correct answer, otherwise 1 mark for using correct equation, 1 mark for correct rearrangement, 1 mark for correctly substituting in all of the values]

Pages 73-75 — Work Done and Power

Warm-up

As a rubber ball falls, it experiences a <u>force</u> due to <u>gravity</u>. <u>Work</u> is done on the ball and <u>energy</u> is transferred from the ball's <u>gravitational potential</u> energy store to its <u>kinetic</u> energy store.

1   B *[1 mark]*

2 a) $t = 125 \times 60 = 7500$ seconds
        $P = E \div t$ so $E = Pt = 600 \times 7500 = 4\,500\,000 = \mathbf{4500\ kJ}$
        [4 marks for the correct answer, otherwise 1 mark for correct equation, 1 mark for the correct substitution, 1 mark for correct conversion to kJ]

   b)   Time taken = $125 \times 60 = 7500$ seconds
        $P = E \div t = 3\,930\,000 \div 7500 = \mathbf{524\ W}$
        [2 marks for correct answer, otherwise 1 mark for correct substitution]

3 a) i)   Work done = force applied × distance moved in the direction of the force *[1 mark]*

     ii) $50 \times 15 = \mathbf{750}$
        [2 marks for correct answer, otherwise 1 mark for correct substitution]

   b)   The temperature of the wheel increases *[1 mark]* because doing work causes some energy to be transferred to the thermal energy store of the wheel *[1 mark]*.

4 a) Efficiency = useful energy transferred by the device
          ÷ total energy supplied to the device
Power is the energy transferred per second,
so in 1 s the old engine transfers 52 000 J usefully.
Total energy supplied to the engine (in 1 second)
= useful energy transferred by the engine ÷ efficiency
= 52 000 ÷ 0.25 = 208 000 J
For the new engine:
Useful energy transferred by the engine (in 1 second)
= efficiency × total energy supplied to the engine
= 0.30 × 208 000 = 62 400 J
So every second, the new engine outputs 62 400 J of energy.
Power is energy per second, so the output power of the new engine
is **62 400 W**.
*[5 marks for correct answer, otherwise 1 mark for correct efficiency
equation, 1 mark for finding total energy supplied to the engine,
1 mark for converting efficiency to a decimal, 1 mark for correctly
substituting into the efficiency equation at any point]*
*You could also have put power = energy ÷ time straight into the efficiency equation
to get efficiency = power output ÷ power input and then used this for your
calculations.*

b) It will decrease the time *[1 mark]* because more energy is being
transferred to the kinetic energy store of the car per second *[1 mark]*.
This decreases the time needed for enough energy to be in the car's
kinetic energy store to cause it to travel at 20 m/s *[1 mark]*.

5 a) How to grade your answer:
Level 0: There is no relevant information. *[No marks]*
Level 1: There are some relevant points, but the answer is unclear.
          There is some description of the experimental set-up,
          but the details are unclear. There are explanations of the
          measurements and calculations that should be made, but
          they may be incomplete. The points made are basic and
          not linked together. *[1 to 2 marks]*
Level 2: There is a more detailed description of the experimental
          set-up, and there is some explanation of the
          measurements and calculations that should be made.
          There is also an explanation of how the student can
          ensure validity in the results, but it may be incomplete.
          Some of the points made are linked together. *[3-4 marks]*
Level 3: There is a clear and detailed description of how the
          equipment listed should be set up and used to carry out
          an experiment safely. There are full explanations of the
          measurements and calculations that should be made to
          determine the useful output power of the motor.
          There is also a full explanation of how the student can
          ensure validity in the results. The points are well-linked
          and the answer has a clear and logical structure.
          [5 to 6 marks]
Here are some points your answer may include:
Securely attach the clamp stand to the edge of
a bench/worktop.
Set up the motor so that it is connected to the circuit, and clamped
to the clamp stand. Make sure there is at least a metre of clear space
between the motor and the ground.
Attach one end of the string to the axle of the motor (so that it will
wind around the axle when the motor spins).
Attach the other end of the string to the 1 kg mass securely, so it
hangs from the string.
Set up the ruler to stand vertically, parallel to the string.
Attach a marker to the bottom of the mass so that the distance moved
by the mass can be accurately measured.
Turn on the motor, and, using the stopwatch, record the time taken
for the motor to lift the mass through a fixed vertical height, e.g.
60 cm, measured by the metre ruler.
Repeat this at least two more times, and calculate an average value of
the time taken from the three results.
Use the height to calculate the change in gravitational potential
energy of the mass, and so the useful energy transferred by the
motor.
Calculate the useful power by dividing this value of energy by the
average value of time taken.
Valid results are repeatable and reproducible and answer the original
question. To ensure the results are valid, the student must make the
experiment a fair test by identifying the control variables and keeping
them constant. E.g. the same equipment should be used for all
repeats, and the same person should operate the stopwatch each time.

b) i) 0.01 s *[1 mark]*
   ii) The errors in the student's time measurements will mostly be caused
        by human error and her reaction time *[1 mark]*. Human reaction
        times are typically much larger than the smallest time measured by
        the stopwatch (0.2-0.6 s compared to 0.01 s) *[1 mark]*.

Pages 76-77 — Forces

1 a) i) E.g. a force that acts between objects that are touching *[1 mark]*.
     ii) Any two from: e.g. friction / normal contact force / air resistance
          [2 marks — 1 mark for each correct answer]
  b) E.g. gravitational force / magnetic force / electrostatic force *[1 mark]*
2 C *[1 mark]*
3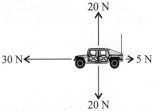
*[1 mark for correct directions of forces, 1 mark for arrows drawn to
scale]*

4 a)
*[1 mark for correct arrow length (same as 30 N
arrow length), 1 mark for correct direction]*
  b) 100 N *[1 mark]*
*As the ladder isn't moving, there must be a resultant force of zero acting on it. This
means that the weight of the ladder must equal the vertical force between the ladder
and the ground.*

5 a)
*[1 mark for correct arrow length (same as the arrow
on magnet B), 1 mark for correct direction]*
  b) E.g. the magnetic fields of the two magnets interacting *[1 mark]*.
  c) Both arrows need to be longer
      (to indicate the stronger interaction) *[1 mark]*.
      The arrows need to be the same size as each other *[1 mark]*.
*The repulsion forces between the magnets are an interaction pair — so they are
always equal in size but act in the opposite direction to each other.*

Pages 78-79 — Forces and Vector Diagrams

Warm-up
Horizontal component = 4 N
Vertical component = 3 N
1 a) 1 cm = 100 N *[1 mark]*
  b)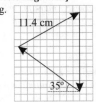

1 cm = 100 N, so 4.3 cm = 4.3 × 100 = 430 N
Magnitude = **430 N (accept between 420 N and 440 N)**
*[1 mark for correct construction of resultant force, 1 mark for
correct magnitude]*
2 E.g.

Scale for drawing: 1 cm = 50 N
Length of 620 N force: 620 ÷ 50 = 12.4 cm
Length of 610 force: 610 ÷ 50 = 12.2 cm
Length of force X = 11.4 cm
11.4 × 50 = 570 N
Magnitude of force X = **570 N (accept between 565 and 575)**
Direction = **062 °** (accept between 61 and 63 °)
*[1 mark for using a sensible scale, 1 mark for correctly drawing a
closed shape, 1 mark for vector arrows the correct length and in the
correct direction, 1 mark for correct magnitude of force X, 1 mark
for direction of force as a bearing]*

Pages 80-81 — Moments

1 Cog B: clockwise ***[1 mark]***
Cog C: anticlockwise ***[1 mark]***

2 a) The turning effect of a force ***[1 mark]***.

b) moment = 50 × 0.12 = **6**
Unit: **Nm**
[3 marks for the correct answer, otherwise 1 mark for a correct substitution, 1 mark for correct numerical value or 1 mark for the correct unit]

3 Moment created by child on plank = force × distance
= 420 × 0.60 = 252 Nm

To move the child:
Moment at P = 252 Nm
Force at P = moment ÷ distance = 252 ÷ 2.4 = **105 N**
[3 marks for correct answer, otherwise 1 mark for correct calculation of the moment created by the child on the plank, 1 mark for correct rearrangement and substitution to find force at point P]

4 Ratio of teeth between cogs A and B = 9 : 3 = 3 : 1
So for 1 complete turn of cog A, cog B completes **3 turns**.
Ratio of teeth between cogs A and C = 9 : 6 = 3 : 2
So for 2 complete turns of cog A, cog C completes 3 turns, so for 1 complete turn of cog A, cog C completes **1.5 turns**.
[3 marks for both correct answers, otherwise 1 mark for finding both ratios]

5 a) E.g. the beam / the unit masses ***[1 mark]***

Control variables are kept the same throughout an experiment to make it a fair test. So in this experiment, he should always use the same beam and the same set of unit masses.

b) A systematic error ***[1 mark]***

c) Total anticlockwise moment:
moment = 80 × 0.20 = 16 Nm
Total clockwise moment:
$(150 \times 0.10) + (20 \times x) = 15 + 20x$
The beam is balanced, so the sum of the anticlockwise moments is equal to the sum of the clockwise moments.
$16 = 15 + 20x$
$20x = 16 - 15$, so $20x = 1$
$x = 1 \div 20 = 0.05 =$ **5 cm**
[5 marks for the correct answer, otherwise 1 mark for calculating the total anticlockwise moment, 1 mark for calculating the total clockwise moment, 1 mark for equating them and 1 mark for the correct rearrangement]

Section 7 — Electricity and Circuits

Page 82 — Current and Circuits

Warm-up
Current is the rate of flow of electric charge (electrons) around a circuit. A current will flow around a circuit if the circuit is closed and there is a source of potential difference.
The current flowing through a component increases when the potential difference across it increases or when the resistance of the component decreases.

1 B ***[1 mark]***

2 a) charge = current × time
= 3.5 × 120 = **420 C**
[3 marks for correct answer, otherwise 1 mark for using the correct equation, 1 mark for substituting in correct values]

b) Rearrange charge = current × time for time:
time = charge ÷ current
= 770 ÷ 3.5 = **220 s**
[3 marks for correct answer, otherwise 1 mark for rearranging charge equation for time, 1 mark for substituting in the correct values]

Page 83 — Potential Difference and Resistance

Warm-up
True, False, True

1 a) $E = Q \times V$, so
$Q = E \div V = 276\ 000 \div 230 =$ **1200 C**
[3 marks for correct answer, otherwise 1 mark for rearranging energy transferred equation for charge, 1 mark for correctly substituting in the values]

b) $E = Q \times V = 1000 \times 230 = 230\ 000 =$ **230 kJ**
[2 marks for correct answer, otherwise 1 mark for correctly substituting in the values]

2 a) $V = IR$ so $R = V \div I$
$R = 18 \div 3 =$ **6 Ω**
[4 marks for correct answer, otherwise 1 mark for correctly rearranging the equation for resistance, 1 mark for substituting in the correct values, 1 mark for correct value, or 1 mark for correct unit]

b) When current flows through the resistor, electrons collide with the ions in the lattice of the resistor ***[1 mark]***. This transfers energy to the ions ***[1 mark]*** causing them to vibrate more and causing the resistor to heat up ***[1 mark]***. The more the ions vibrate, the harder it is for the electrons to pass through the lattice, so the current decreases ***[1 mark]***.

Pages 84-85 — Investigating Components

1 a) D ***[1 mark]***

b)

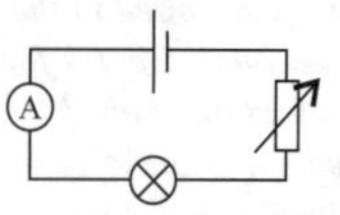

[1 mark for an ammeter anywhere in series on the circuit]

2 a) It is used to alter the output potential difference of the source/current in the circuit ***[1 mark]*** so that pairs of readings of potential difference across the filament lamp and current through it can be measured ***[1 mark]***.

b) This will prevent the circuit from heating up too much ***[1 mark]*** which could increase the resistance, leading to the results being inaccurate ***[1 mark]***.

3 a) E.g. adjust the variable resistor to change the current through the circuit. Record the current through the diode using the ammeter, and the potential difference across it using the voltmeter ***[1 mark]***. Use the equation $V = IR$ (in the form $R = V \div I$) to calculate the resistance of the diode at this current using the current and potential difference measurements ***[1 mark]***. Repeat this for a number of different values of current (e.g. at least 6), changing the current by a fixed amount each time (e.g. 1 mA) ***[1 mark]***.

b) E.g.

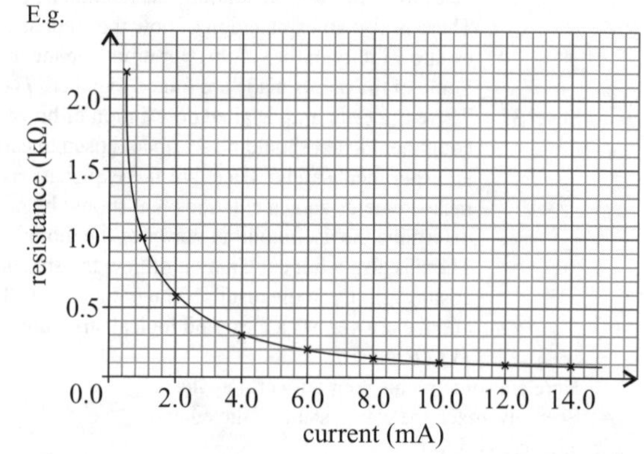

[1 mark for smooth line passing through or close to all points]

c) E.g. she has only carried out the experiment for positive values of current / current flowing in one direction ***[1 mark]***. This means she cannot make a conclusion about the effect of the size of the current, because the device may behave differently for current that flows in the opposite direction / because diodes are known to have a very high resistance for one direction of current flow but not the opposite ***[1 mark]***.

Page 86 — Circuit Devices

Warm-up
From top to bottom: LDR, diode, thermistor

1 a) The resistance decreases ***[1 mark]***.

b) E.g. temperature detectors in thermostats/car engines ***[1 mark]***.

2 a) B ***[1 mark]***

b) E.g. when the current increases, so does the temperature of the filament ***[1 mark]***. This makes the resistance increase, so the graph is curved ***[1 mark]***.

Pages 87-89 — Series and Parallel Circuits

1 A ***[1 mark]***

2   E.g.

[1 mark for using the correct symbols for an LDR and a cell, 1 mark for correctly drawing the LDRs in parallel]

3 a) $10 + 30 = \mathbf{40\ \Omega}$ *[1 mark]*

   b) $V = IR$

          $V = 0.075 \times 30 = \mathbf{2.25\ V}$

          [3 marks for a correct answer, otherwise 1 mark for quoting the correct equation, 1 mark for substituting in the correct values]

4   How to grade your answer:

Level 0:   There is no relevant information. *[0 marks]*

Level 1:   There is a brief explanation about the effect of adding resistors in series or parallel. The points made are basic and not linked together. *[1-2 marks]*

Level 2:   There is a comparison between adding resistors in series and parallel and an explanation of their effects. Some of the points made are linked together. *[3-4 marks]*

Level 3:   A logical and detailed comparison is given, explaining why adding resistors in series increases the total resistance but adding them in parallel reduces it. The points made are well-linked and the answer has a clear and logical structure. *[5-6 marks]*

Here are some points your answer may include:

In series, resistors share the potential difference from the power source.

The more resistors that are in series, the lower the potential difference across each one, and so the lower the current through each resistor (as $V = IR$).

Current is the same all around a series circuit, so adding a resistor will decrease the current for the whole circuit.

A decrease in total current means an increase in total resistance.

In parallel, all resistors have the same potential difference as the source.

Adding another resistor in parallel (forming another circuit loop) increases the current flowing in the circuit, as there are more paths for the current to flow through.

An increase in total current means a decrease in total resistance (because $V = IR$).

5 a)   Find the equivalent resistance of the circuit:

          potential difference = current × resistance so

          resistance = potential difference ÷ current

                   $= 12 \div 0.25 = 48\ \Omega$

          This is the resistance of both bulbs, so divide by 2:

          $48 \div 2 = \mathbf{24\ \Omega}$

          [3 marks for the correct answer, otherwise 1 mark for rearranging the equation for resistance, 1 mark for using this to correctly calculate the equivalent resistance of the circuit]

   b) i)   First find the current through the circuit branch with bulb 3:

          potential difference = current × resistance, so

          current = potential difference ÷ resistance

                   $= 12 \div 24 = 0.5\ A$

          0.25 A is still flowing through the branch with bulbs 1 and 2. Then find the current through ammeter by adding the currents flowing through each branch:

          current = $0.5 + 0.25 = \mathbf{0.75\ A}$

          [2 marks for correct answer, otherwise 1 mark for calculating the current for the branch with bulb 3]

The current flowing through the branch with bulbs 1 and 2 on it doesn't change when bulb 3 is added, as the resistance of this branch and the potential difference across it don't change.

     ii)   Because the potential difference across bulb 3 is the same as the source potential difference, but bulbs 1 and 2 share the source potential difference *[1 mark]*, so the current through bulb 3 is higher *[1 mark]*.

   c) i)   The current through the ammeter decreases *[1 mark]*.

     ii)   The brightness of bulbs 1 and 2 doesn't change *[1 mark]*. Bulb 3 gets dimmer *[1 mark]*.

   d)   Because the bulbs may not have been identical *[1 mark]*. Because the bulbs may have got hotter as the experiment went on, which would increase their resistance *[1 mark]*.

Page 90 — Energy in Circuits

1   D *[1 mark]*

2 a)   The heating element *[1 mark]*.

   b)   In the wires / in the motor *[1 mark]*.

   c)   The longer the hairdryer is on for, the more the motor/wires heat up *[1 mark]*. This increases the resistance of the wires/ motor *[1 mark]*, meaning less energy is transferred usefully *[1 mark]*.

3 a) $E = I \times V \times t$

          so $t = E \div (I \times V) = 355\ 000 \div (12 \times 230) = 128.623...$

               $= \mathbf{129\ s}$ **(to the nearest second)**

          [3 marks for correct answer, otherwise 1 mark for correctly rearranging the equation for time, 1 mark for calculating a value of 128.623...s]

   b)   E.g. that the kettle was 100% efficient / that all the energy transferred to the kettle was used heating the water / that no energy was transferred to heating the wires/surroundings *[1 mark]*.

Page 91 — Power in Circuits

1 a) $E = P \times t$

          $E = 50 \times 20 = \mathbf{1000\ J}$

          [3 marks for correct answer, otherwise 1 mark for using the correct equation, 1 mark for correctly substituting the values into the equation]

   b)   The power of the car is higher *[1 mark]*. So more energy is transferred away from the chemical energy store of the battery per second *[1 mark]*.

2 a) $P = I \times V$

          so $I = P \div V = 75 \div 230 = 0.3260... = \mathbf{0.33\ A}$ **(to 2 s.f.)**

          [3 marks for the correct answer rounded to 1 or 2 significant figures, otherwise 1 mark for rearranging the equation for current, 1 mark for calculating a value of 0.3260... A]

   b) $P = I^2 \times R$ so $R = \dfrac{P}{I^2} = 2.5 \div 0.50^2 = \mathbf{10\ \Omega}$

          [3 marks for correct answer, otherwise 1 mark for rearranging the equation for resistance, 1 mark for substituting in the correct values]

   c) i)   model A *[1 mark]*

     ii)   Because it is very noisy *[1 mark]* which means it may be transferring a lot of energy away as sound, making it less efficient *[1 mark]*.

Pages 92-93 — Electricity in the Home

Warm-up

From top to bottom:

Direct current, alternating current, alternating current, direct current

1 a)   230 V, 50 Hz *[1 mark]*

   b) i)   Live: brown

          Neutral: blue

          Earth: green and yellow

          [2 marks for all three correct, otherwise 1 mark for two correct]

     ii)   Live wire and neutral wire — 230 V

          Neutral wire and earth wire — 0 V

          Earth wire and live wire — 230 V

          [1 mark for each correct potential difference]

2   No, the radio won't work *[1 mark]*. A closed loop has been formed, where current from the live wire is carried away by the neutral wire *[1 mark]*, so no (or very little) current will flow through the radio *[1 mark]*.

3 a)   To stop an electric current from flowing out of the live wire and potentially causing an electric shock (i.e. for safety) *[1 mark]*. To make it easy to identify the live wire *[1 mark]*.

   b)   The man has an electric potential of 0 V *[1 mark]* and the wire has an electric potential (of 230 V) so a potential difference exists between them *[1 mark]*. This causes a current to flow through the man *[1 mark]*.

   c)   Yes *[1 mark]*. Although there is no current flowing when it is switched off, there is still a potential difference in the live wire inside the socket *[1 mark]*. Touching it could cause a current to flow through you to the Earth *[1 mark]*.

Page 94 — Fuses and Earthing

1 a)   To protect the wiring of the house and prevent fires in the event of a fault *[1 mark]*.

   b)   Because pennies won't melt like a fuse wire in the event of a current surge, so the circuit won't be broken *[1 mark]*.

   c)   Advantage: e.g. circuit breakers break the circuit more quickly than fuses / circuit breakers are easier to reset that fuses *[1 mark]*. Disadvantage: e.g. circuit breakers are more expensive than fuses *[1 mark]*.

2 a) If the live wire comes loose and touches the metal, a large current will flow through the fuse, the live wire and the earth wire *[1 mark]*. This current melts the thin wire in the fuse *[1 mark]*, cutting off the electricity supply to the device *[1 mark]*.

b) The fuse needs to be rated slightly higher than the normal operating current of the device *[1 mark]*, and the electric heater has a higher operating current than the clock radio *[1 mark]*.

Section 8 — Electric and Magnetic Fields

Page 95 — Static Electricity

1 a) When the rod is rubbed with the cloth, electrons are transferred from the rod to the cloth *[1 mark]*. Acetate/plastic is an insulator, so a positive static charge builds up *[1 mark]*.

b) i) When the positive rod is held near the scraps of paper, it slightly repels the positive charges in the paper *[1 mark]*. This induces a negative charge on the surface of the paper *[1 mark]* so the paper is attracted towards the rod, and 'jumps' towards it *[1 mark]*.

ii) Metal is a conductor *[1 mark]* so when it's rubbed with a cloth, electrons will just flow through it, so no static charge builds up on it/it stays neutral *[1 mark]* and can't induce a charge in the paper *[1 mark]*.

2 a) The man is charged, so there is a potential difference between him and the rail *[1 mark]*. When the potential difference is high enough, electrons jump across the gap to the rail, producing a spark *[1 mark]*.

b) Negatively charged *[1 mark]*. Only negative charges/electrons can move *[1 mark]* and they will move from an area of negative charge to an earthed area *[1 mark]*.

Page 96 — Uses and Dangers of Static Electricity

Warm-up

Electrostatic sprayers work by electrically charging droplets of paint. The charge on each drop is <u>the same as</u> the charge on the other drops, so they <u>repel</u> each other. This means you get a very fine spray. The charge on the object being painted is <u>opposite to</u> the charge of the paint droplets, so it <u>attracts</u> them.

1 Ice and water droplets rub together and cause electrons to be moved between them *[1 mark]*. This causes a static charge to build up inside the cloud — the top of the cloud has the opposite charge to the bottom of the cloud *[1 mark]*. This creates a large potential difference, which leads to a spark (lightning) *[1 mark]*.

2 a) If a large static charge builds up, it could cause a spark *[1 mark]* which could cause a fire/an explosion *[1 mark]*.

b) Connect the fuel tanker to the ground with an earth wire *[1 mark]* as this allows charge to flow to/away from the tanker and stops static electricity building up *[1 mark]*.

Pages 97-98 — Electric Fields

1 a) B *[1 mark]*

b)
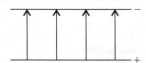

[1 mark for at least three straight, parallel lines equally spaced between the two plates, 1 mark for at least two arrows showing the correct direction of the field]

c) i)
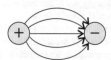

[1 mark for correctly labelling both spheres]

ii) The charges would move towards each other *[1 mark]*.

d) i)

[1 mark for at least eight straight lines from the charge, 1 mark for lines equally spaced, 1 mark for at least two arrows showing the correct direction and pointing to the centre of the charge]

ii) It decreases *[1 mark]*.

iii) They would be pointing away from the charge instead of towards it *[1 mark]*.

2 a) The size of the force increases *[1 mark]*.

b) The negative electrons are attracted towards the positive sphere, while the positive nucleus is attracted towards the negative cube *[1 mark]*. So parts of the particle are pulled away from each other *[1 mark]*. When the potential difference is high enough, the force becomes large enough to break the particle apart *[1 mark]*.

c) A current can easily flow through the air now it is ionised *[1 mark]*, so a spark jumps between the cube and the sphere *[1 mark]*.

Pages 99-100 — Magnets and Magnetic Fields

Warm-up
T, F, T

1 a) C *[1 mark]*

b)
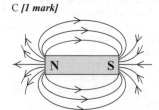

[1 mark for at least two lines between the north and south poles, 1 mark for at least three lines at each pole, 1 mark for at least one arrow in the correct direction with no arrows in the incorrect direction]

c) i) E.g. a uniform field has the same strength everywhere / the field lines are parallel and equally spaced *[1 mark]*

ii)
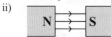

[1 mark for at least three straight, evenly spaced field lines, 1 mark for at least one arrow in the right direction with no arrows in the incorrect direction]

2 A force is acting on both magnets (due to their interacting magnetic fields) *[1 mark]*. This force is repulsive — the magnetic field lines of both objects are travelling away from each other *[1 mark]*. So the two objects move away from each other *[1 mark]*.

3 a) E.g. the needle of a compass points in the direction of the magnetic field it is in *[1 mark]*. Put the magnet on a sheet of paper and place a compass near to it. Mark where the north pole of the compass is pointing *[1 mark]*. Move the compass so its south pole is next to the mark, and again mark where the north pole of the compass is pointing. Repeat this until you've moved the compass around the entire magnet *[1 mark]*. Join up these marks to create a diagram of the magnetic field lines *[1 mark]*.

b) It would point north *[1 mark]* because it is aligning itself with the magnetic field of the Earth *[1 mark]*.

Page 101 — Permanent and Induced Magnets

1 a) E.g. a permanent magnet produces its own magnetic field at all times *[1 mark]*. An induced magnet only produces a magnetic field when it is close to another magnet *[1 mark]*.

b) Any two from: e.g. iron / steel / cobalt / nickel *[2 marks — 1 mark for each correct answer]*

c) E.g. cranes in scrapyards *[1 mark]* use induced electromagnets to pick up, move and put down scrap metal *[1 mark]*.

2 a) The block of cobalt becomes an induced magnet when it is placed in the magnetic field of the bar magnet *[1 mark]*. The magnetic field of the cobalt then makes the paperclip an induced magnet *[1 mark]*, which causes a force of attraction between the paperclip and the cobalt *[1 mark]*.

b) When the bar magnet is removed, the cobalt will quickly demagnetise *[1 mark]*, so the paperclip will become unstuck *[1 mark]*.

Pages 102-103 — Electromagnetism and the Motor Effect

Warm-up
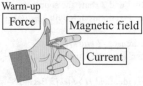

1 a) C *[1 mark]*

Use Fleming's left-hand rule here. Point your first finger in the direction of the field (i.e. from the north pole to the south pole of the magnets). Point your second finger in the direction of the current (shown in the diagram). Your thumb will then show the direction of motion of the wire.

b) The current in the wire creates its own magnetic field *[1 mark]* which interacts with the magnetic field between the poles of the magnets (which results in a force) *[1 mark]*.

c) E.g. the size of the current going through the wire / the strength of the magnetic field that the wire is in / the length of wire inside the magnetic field.
[3 marks — 1 mark for each correct answer]

2 a)

[1 mark for concentric circles around the wire, 1 mark for at least one arrow showing the direction of the field]

b) The direction of the field will also be reversed *[1 mark]*.

c) E.g. increase the current *[1 mark]*.

3 $F = BIl$ so $B = F \div Il$
$B = 1.2 \div (0.4 \times 0.75) = \mathbf{4}$
Unit = **T** or **N/Am**
[4 marks for correct answer, otherwise 1 mark for rearranging, 1 mark for correct substitution, 1 mark for correct numerical value, 1 mark for the correct unit]

Page 104 — Motors and Solenoids

1 a) E.g. a magnet which can be controlled (turned on and off) by an electric current *[1 mark]*.

b) i) E.g. the magnetic field is strong *[1 mark]* and almost uniform *[1 mark]*.

ii) E.g. the magnetic field is weak *[1 mark]* and is a similar shape to that of a bar magnet *[1 mark]*.

2 a) E.g. the interacting magnetic fields (of the coil and the magnets) causes a force on each arm of the coil *[1 mark]*. As the current is travelling in opposite directions in each arm of the coil, the forces created are in opposite directions (which causes the coil to rotate) *[1 mark]*.

b) E.g. swap the contacts every half turn (e.g. using a split-ring commutator) to reverse the direction of the current *[1 mark]*. This swaps the direction of the forces for each arm and keeps the direction of rotation constant *[1 mark]*.

Pages 105-107 — Electromagnetic Induction in Transformers

Warm-up
Transformers consist of two coils of wire, wrapped around an <u>iron</u> core.
Transformers can change the size of <u>alternating</u> potential differences.
<u>Step-down</u> transformers decrease the output potential difference.
<u>Step-up</u> transformers decrease the output current.

1 C *[1 mark]*

2 $V_p \times I_p = V_s \times I_s$ so $I_s = (V_p \times I_p) \div V_s$
$I_s = (30.0 \times 20.0) \div 40.0 = \mathbf{15\,A}$
[3 marks for correct answer, otherwise 1 mark for correct rearrangement, 1 mark for correct substitution]

3 a) Alternating current *[1 mark]*. As he moves the magnet in, the changing magnetic field induces a potential difference, and so current, in the coil in one direction *[1 mark]*. As he moves it out again, it induces a potential difference, and so current, in the opposite direction *[1 mark]*.

b) Increase the speed that the magnet is moved / use a stronger magnet / have more turns per unit length on the coil.
[3 marks — 1 mark for each correct answer]

4 a) How to grade your answer:

Level 0:	There is no relevant information. *[No marks]*
Level 1:	There is a brief description of how electromagnetic induction can induce a potential difference. The points made are basic and not linked together. *[1-2 marks]*
Level 2:	There is a more detailed description of how electromagnetic induction in transformers can induce a potential difference. Some of the points made are linked together. *[3-4 marks]*
Level 3:	There is a clear detailed description of how electromagnetic induction is used in transformers to induce a potential difference. There is an explanation as to how the increased number of turns leads to an increased output potential difference. The points made are well-linked and the answer has a clear and logical structure. *[5-6 marks]*

Here are some points your answer may include:
A step-up transformer has two coils wrapped around a metal (usually iron) core.
Iron is used because it is easy to magnetise.
When a current flows through a wire, it produces a magnetic field around the wire.
The direction of this magnetic field depends on the direction of the current, so when the current is alternating, the magnetic field produced also alternates.
So an alternating current flowing through the primary coil of the transformer creates an alternating magnetic field in the metal core of the transformer.
As the magnetic field in the metal core is alternating, the magnetic field across the secondary coil is always changing.
This change in magnetic field causes a potential difference to be induced in the secondary coil.
In a step-up transformer, there are more turns on the secondary coil than there are on the primary coil.
This means that the potential difference induced in the secondary coil is larger than the potential difference across the primary coil.

b) In the opposite direction to the (changing) magnetic field that caused it *[1 mark]*.

5 a) E.g. if the exposed wire came into contact with the iron core, it could cause electricity to flow through the core, leading to inaccurate results *[1 mark]*.
The exposed wire could cause an electric shock *[1 mark]*.

b) E.g.

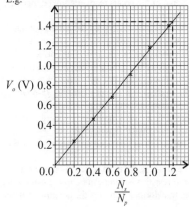

$$\text{gradient} = \frac{\text{change in } y}{\text{change in } x} = \frac{1.44 - 0}{1.24 - 0} \; \text{[1 mark]}$$
$$= 1.1612...$$
$$= \mathbf{1.2\,V} \text{ (to 2 s.f.) } \text{[1 mark]}$$

c) The results do agree with this relationship. E.g. rearranging the relationship to $V_o = V_i \frac{N_s}{N_p}$ and comparing it to the equation of a straight line, it can be seen that a graph of V_o against $\frac{N_s}{N_p}$ should give a straight line through the origin, with a gradient equal to V_i *[1 mark]*. The graph in Figure 3 does pass through the origin *[1 mark]*, and it has a constant gradient which is equal to 1.2 V to 2 significant figures, which is equal to V_i, so it does agree with the relationship *[1 mark]*.

Page 108 — Generators, Microphones and Loudspeakers

Warm-up
An <u>alternating</u> current is passed through a coil of wire that is wrapped around one pole of a <u>permanent</u> magnet and attached to the base of a paper cone. When a current flows, the coil experiences a <u>force</u> which makes the paper cone move.

1 a) D *[1 mark]*

b) It keeps the current flowing in the same direction *[1 mark]*.

2 a)

[1 mark for at least four straight, equally spaced field lines, 1 mark for at least two arrows showing the correct direction and no arrows pointing in the incorrect direction]

b) Sound waves are pressure variations in air, so when they hit the diaphragm it will vibrate/move back and forth *[1 mark]*. This causes the coil to vibrate too, which means it moves back and forth between the magnetic poles *[1 mark]*. This induces an alternating potential difference *[1 mark]* and as the coil is part of a circuit, an alternating current is induced in the circuit, creating electrical signals *[1 mark]*.

Page 109 — Generating and Distributing Electricity

Warm-up
1. boiler, 2. steam, 3. generator, 4. electricity

1
$$\frac{V_s}{V_p} = \frac{N_s}{N_p} \text{ so } N_s = \frac{V_s N_p}{V_p}$$

$N_s = (84 \times 12) \div 245 = 4.114... = $ **4.1 turns (to 2 s.f.)**
[4 marks for correct answer, otherwise 1 mark for correctly rearranging, 1 mark for correct substitution, 1 mark for correct numerical value]

2 How to grade your answer:
Level 0: There is no relevant information. *[No marks]*
Level 1: There is a brief description of an advantage of using transformers or high-voltage cables. The points made are basic and not linked together. *[1-2 marks]*
Level 2: There is a more detailed description of how transferring power at a high voltage results in a lower current and the advantages of this. Some of the points made are linked together. *[3-4 marks]*
Level 3: There is a clear detailed description of the advantages of using transformers and high-voltage cables, as well as correct equations being used to support the answer. The points made are well-linked and the answer has a clear and logical structure. *[5-6 marks]*
Here are some points your answer may include:
Power is the rate of doing work/transferring energy. $P = E \div t$
Power = current × potential difference / $P = IV$
So for a large output power you need either a large current or a large potential difference.
A high current causes energy to be wasted as it heats the cables. The power lost to resistive heating can be found using $P = I^2R$.
Using a step-up transformer increases the potential difference of the output electricity.
As transformers are almost 100% efficient, $V_p \times I_p = V_s \times I_s$
So increasing the output p.d. reduces the output current.
This reduces the power lost / This makes the national grid more efficient.

Section 9 — Matter

Pages 110-111 — Density

1 a) i) $\rho = m \div V$ *[1 mark]*
   ii) $\rho = 10\ 000 \div 0.5 = $ **20 000 kg/m³**
      [2 marks for correct answer, otherwise 1 mark for correct substitution]
   b) The density is the same for the whole block,
      so $\rho = 20\ 000$ kg/m³
      $\rho = m \div V$ so $m = \rho \times V = 20\ 000 \times 0.02 = $ **400 kg**
      [2 marks for correct answer, otherwise 1 mark for correct substitution]

2 volume = area × length = 0.050 × 0.40 = 0.02 m³
  $\rho = m \div V = 90.0 \div 0.02 = $ **4500 kg/m³**
  [3 marks for correct answer, otherwise 1 mark for calculating the volume of the bar, 1 mark for correct substitution into equation for density]

3 $\rho = m \div V$
  1 ml of water = 1 cm³
  A: $\rho = 5.7 \div 0.30 = 19$ g/cm³. So A is gold.
  B: $\rho = 2.7 \div 0.60 = 4.5$ g/cm³. So B is titanium.
  C: $\rho = 3.0 \div 0.30 = 10$ g/cm³. So C is silver.
  [5 marks for correct answer, otherwise 1 mark for stating 1 ml = 1 cm³, 1 mark for correct substitutions and 1 mark for each correct conclusion]

4 Measure the mass (m_1) of the object using the mass balance *[1 mark]*. Fill the bottle with a liquid of a known density. Measure the mass of the filled bottle (m_2) *[1 mark]*. Empty the bottle and place the object inside it. Fill it with the same liquid as before. Measure the mass of the bottle again (m_3) *[1 mark]*. Calculate the mass of the liquid displaced by the object ($m_2 - [m_3 - m_1]$) *[1 mark]* then use this to calculate the volume of the liquid displaced from $V = m \div \rho$, where ρ is the density of the liquid, (which equals the volume of the object) *[1 mark]*. Use this volume and the mass of the object to calculate its density using $\rho = m \div V$ *[1 mark]*.

Pages 112-113 — Kinetic Theory and States of Matter

Warm-up
From left to right: liquid, solid, gas

1 condensation — gas to liquid
  sublimation — solid to gas
  evaporation — liquid to gas
  [1 mark for all 3 correct]

2 a) C *[1 mark]*
  b) There is a smaller mass (and so fewer particles) in a given volume of ice than of water *[1 mark]*. So the water molecules are further apart in ice than they are in liquid water *[1 mark]*.
  Substances are usually more dense as a solid than as a liquid, but water is an exception to this.

3 a) It has evaporated/it has become water vapour *[1 mark]*.
  b) The total mass stays the same *[1 mark]* because all of the particles are still in the flask/its a closed system *[1 mark]*.

4 As the water is heated, energy is transferred from its thermal energy store to the thermal energy store of the methanol *[1 mark]*. This means the methanol particles have more energy in their kinetic energy stores *[1 mark]*, so will move around more — causing the methanol to increase in volume and move the piston *[1 mark]*. As energy is continuously being transferred to them, some particles gain enough energy to overcome their attraction to each other *[1 mark]* and some of the methanol changes state into a gas *[1 mark]*.

Pages 114-115 — Specific Heat Capacity

Warm-up
The energy needed to raise 1 kg of a substance by 1 °C.

1 a) i) The time taken for the liquid to heat *[1 mark]*.
      The mass of the liquid *[1 mark]*.
   ii) Calculate the change in temperature by subtracting the temperature before from the temperature after *[1 mark]*.
      Calculate the change in thermal energy using
      energy transferred = current × potential difference × time *[1 mark]*.
      Calculate specific heat capacity by rearranging
      change in thermal energy =
      mass × specific heat capacity × change in temperature *[1 mark]*.
   b) $\Delta Q = mc\Delta\theta$ so $c = \Delta Q \div m\Delta\theta$
      $= 6000 \div (0.3 \times 10)$
      Specific heat capacity = **2000 J/kg °C**
      [3 marks for correct answer, otherwise 1 mark for rearranging, 1 mark for correct substitution]

2 a) Yes, he is correct. The foam will serve as insulation, which will reduce the transfer of energy away from the block while it is being heated *[1 mark]*. This means the student's energy measurements will more accurately reflect the amount of energy that is transferred to the block and causes an increase in temperature *[1 mark]*.
  b) Material C has the highest specific heat capacity *[1 mark]*. E.g. The higher the specific heat capacity of a material, the more energy is required to increase the temperature of 1 kg of the material by 1 °C *[1 mark]*. Material C had the smallest increase in temperature when the same amount of energy was transferred to the same mass of each material, so it must have the highest specific heat capacity *[1 mark]*.
  You could also have answered this question using the specific heat capacity equation.

  $\Delta Q = mc\Delta\theta$, so the gradient of the graph is equal to $\frac{1}{mc}$.

  Since m is the same for all of the materials, this means the line with the shallowest gradient shows the highest specific heat capacity.
  c) Valid results are repeatable and reproducible. To confirm that his results are repeatable, the student should repeat the experiment with the same method, and check that he gets very similar results *[1 mark]*. To confirm his results are reproducible, he should repeat the experiment using different equipment and/or a different experimental method, and check that he gets very similar results *[1 mark]*.

Pages 116-117 — Specific Latent Heat

1   D *[1 mark]*

2 a)   The amount of energy required to change the state of one kilogram of a substance with no change in temperature *[1 mark]*.

 b)   E.g. specific heat capacity is the energy needed to cause a temperature rise without causing a change of state, but specific latent heat is the energy needed to cause a change of state, where the temperature remains constant *[1 mark]*.

 c)   −2 °C *[1 mark]*

3 a)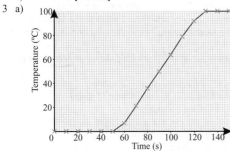

   [1 mark for all points plotted correctly, 1 mark for a correctly drawn line connecting the points]

 b)   500 g = 0.5 kg
   $Q = m \times L$ so $L = Q \div m$
   $L = 1.13 \div 0.5 =$ **2.26 MJ/kg**
   [3 marks for correct answer, otherwise 1 mark for rearranging, 1 mark for correct substitution]

 c)   As the substance is heated, energy is transferred to the kinetic energy stores of its particles *[1 mark]*. As the substance melts (from 0 to 50 s), all of this energy is used to break apart the intermolecular bonds between the particles *[1 mark]* so there is no increase in the substance's temperature as it changes state *[1 mark]*.

Pages 118-119 — Particle Motion in Gases

Warm-up

The particles in a gas are always moving in <u>random directions</u>.
A gas exerts a force on a container due to <u>collisions</u>.
The total force exerted by the particles per unit area is the gas <u>pressure</u>.

1   Absolute zero is the temperature at which particles barely move / the temperature at which particles have the smallest amount of energy possible in their kinetic energy stores *[1 mark]*.

2   Container A holds the same number of particles, travelling at the same speed, as container B, but in a larger volume *[1 mark]*. This means the particles hit the walls of container A less often and so exert less pressure *[1 mark]*.

3 a)   295 − 273 = **22 °C** *[1 mark]*

 b)   The pressure of the gas increases *[1 mark]*. This is because increasing the temperature of the gas increases the speed of the gas particles *[1 mark]* so they collide with the walls of the container more often and with more force *[1 mark]*.

4   D *[1 mark]*
The volume of each container is the same (0.04 m³ = 40 000 cm³). Container D has the highest temperature (the temperature of container C is 283 − 273 = 10 °C). A fixed mass and volume of a gas has a higher pressure at a higher temperature.

5 a) $P_1V_1 = P_2V_2$ so $P_2 = P_1V_1 \div V_2$
   Use the data from the first row of the table to find the missing pressure:
   $P_2 = (50 \times 10^3) \times (8.0 \times 10^{-4}) \div (1.6 \times 10^{-4})$
   $= 250\ 000 =$ **250 kPa**
   [3 marks for correct answer, otherwise 1 mark for correctly rearranging the equation and 1 mark for correctly substituting in values.]
You could have used any row from the table to help you find the missing value — as long as you did the calculation correctly you'd get the marks.

 b)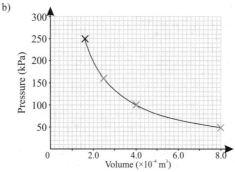

   [1 mark for correctly plotted point, 1 mark for a curved line connecting them]

Page 120 — Pressure, Temperature and Volume

1   D *[1 mark]*

2 a)   The volume of the helium increases as the plunger is moved outwards, and the temperature of the helium remains constant, so the speed of its particles doesn't change *[1 mark]*. This results in the pressure of the helium decreasing as the plunger is moved outwards *[1 mark]*. The outward pressure from the helium inside the syringe is now less than the inward pressure on the plunger from the air outside the syringe *[1 mark]* so the plunger moves down the syringe when it is released. This decreases the volume of the helium, so increases its pressure *[1 mark]* until it is equal to the air pressure, and the plunger stops moving *[1 mark]*.

 b)   The helium exerts a pressure, and therefore a force, on the plunger *[1 mark]*. Work is done against this force when the plunger is pushed down *[1 mark]*. This transfers energy to the kinetic energy stores of the helium particles *[1 mark]*, which could increase the temperature of the helium gas *[1 mark]*.

Pages 121-122 — Forces and Elasticity

1 a)   Two *[1 mark]*

 b)   An object that has been elastically distorted will go back to its original shape and length when the distorting forces are removed *[1 mark]*. An object that has been inelastically distorted won't *[1 mark]*.

 c) i) $F = kx$ *[1 mark]*

 ii) $k = F \div x = 20 \div 0.08 =$ **250 N/m**
   [2 marks for correct answer, otherwise 1 mark for correct substitution]

 d)   That stretching the spring by 8 cm doesn't exceed its limit of proportionality *[1 mark]*.

2   D *[1 mark]*

3 a)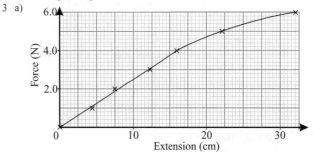

   [1 mark for points plotted correctly, 1 mark for line of best fit showing linear relationship between 0 cm and at least 12 cm, 1 mark for curved line of best fit towards the end of the graph]

 b) $F = kx$
   so $k = F \div x =$ gradient of the linear section of the graph
   $k = 3.0 \div 0.12 =$ **25 N/m**
   [2 marks for correct answer between 24 and 26 N/m, otherwise 1 mark for correct calculation]

 c)   The limit of proportionality is exceeded when the relationship between force and extension becomes non-linear *[1 mark]*. This is shown by the graph beginning to curve *[1 mark]*.

 d)   When he was loading the spring he distorted the spring inelastically *[1 mark]* so when the force was removed, the spring didn't return to its original length *[1 mark]*.
You could also refer to the student exceeding the elastic limit of the spring, which would mean it was inelastically distorted.

Page 123 — Fluid Pressure

1 a) pressure = force ÷ area *[1 mark]*

  b) $P = F \div A = 12 \div 0.15 =$ **80 Pa**
[2 marks for correct answer, otherwise 1 mark for correct substitution]

2 a) $P = h\rho g$ so
$\rho = P \div hg = 2850 \div (0.15 \times 10)$
$= $ **1900 kg/m³**
[3 marks for correct answer, otherwise 1 mark for correctly rearranging the equation for density, 1 mark for correct substitution]

  b) Liquid B is denser than water, so it has more particles in a given volume *[1 mark]*. This means there are more collisions of liquid particles on a given surface for liquid B than for water, so liquid B exerts a higher pressure *[1 mark]*. There are also more particles above a given depth in liquid B *[1 mark]*, meaning the weight of the particles above this depth is larger for liquid B than for water, so the pressure is higher *[1 mark]*.

Page 124 — Upthrust and Atmospheric Pressure

1 When the ball is submerged in the water, upthrust acts upon the ball *[1 mark]*. Upthrust acts in the opposite direction to the ball's weight *[1 mark]* so the resultant downward force is less (so the ball appears to weigh less) *[1 mark]*.

2 When an object is placed in or on water, it experiences upthrust (an upwards force) equal to the weight of water it has displaced *[1 mark]*. If this upthrust is equal to the weight of the object, then the object will float *[1 mark]*, and if it is less than the weight of the object, then the object will sink *[1 mark]*. The boat is less dense than the water, so it displaces a volume of water equal to its weight before it is submerged and therefore it floats *[1 mark]*. The necklace is more dense than water, so it cannot displace a volume of water equal to its weight and it sinks *[1 mark]*.

3 How to grade your answer:
Level 0: There is no relevant information. *[No marks]*
Level 1: There is a brief explanation of the cause of atmospheric pressure. *[1 to 2 marks]*
Level 2: There is some explanation of why atmospheric pressure decreases with altitude. *[3 to 4 marks]*
Level 3: There is a clear and detailed explanation of why atmospheric pressure decreases with altitude. *[5 to 6 marks]*
Here are some points your answer may include:
The atmosphere is a relatively thin layer of air around the Earth.
Atmospheric pressure is caused by air molecules colliding with a surface, which exerts a force on the surface.
As altitude increases, the atmosphere gets less dense (there are fewer air molecules in a given volume).
This means that there are fewer air molecules to collide with a surface, so the force and pressure exerted decrease.
The weight of the air molecules above a surface also contributes to atmospheric pressure.
Because there are fewer air molecules as altitude increases, the weight of the air above a surface will also decrease. So the atmospheric pressure decreases too.

Mixed Questions

Pages 125-135 — Mixed Questions

1 a) metre *[1 mark]*

  b) B *[1 mark]*

  c) A quantity that has a magnitude/size, but not a direction *[1 mark]*.

2 a) B *[1 mark]*

  b) work done = force × distance = $5 \times 10 =$ **50 J**
[2 marks for correct answer, otherwise 1 mark for correct substitution]

3 a) A *[1 mark]*

  b) average speed = distance travelled ÷ time
$= 420 \div (5 \times 60) =$ **1.4 m/s**
[3 marks for correct answer, otherwise 1 mark for correct substitution, 1 mark for correct numerical answer, 1 mark for correct unit]

  c) B *[1 mark]*

4 a) E.g. sound / P-waves *[1 mark]*

  b) X-ray: e.g. medical imaging/diagnosing broken bones / airport security scanners *[1 mark]*.
Gamma rays: e.g. sterilising food/medical equipment / tracers / radiotherapy/treating cancer *[1 mark]*.

  c) A = 99 *[1 mark]*
B = 0 *[1 mark]*

5 a) B *[1 mark]*

  b) D *[1 mark]*

  c) i) potential difference = current × resistance *[1 mark]*

    ii) $R = V \div I = 0.7 \div 0.1 =$ **7 Ω**
[2 marks for correct answer, otherwise 1 mark for correct substitution]

6 a) $v = f\lambda$
so $v = (3 \times 10^{14}) \times (1 \times 10^{-6}) = 300\,000\,000 = $ **3 × 10⁸ m/s**
[4 marks for correct answer, otherwise 1 mark for correct equation, 1 mark for correct substitution, 1 mark for answer not in standard form]

  b) 3×10^8 m/s *[1 mark for answer matching the speed calculated in part a)]*

All electromagnetic waves travel at the same speed in a vacuum.

7 a) E.g. photographic film / Geiger-Müller tube *[1 mark]*

  b) alpha particle — a helium nucleus
beta-minus particle — an electron emitted from the nucleus
gamma ray — an electromagnetic wave
[1 mark for all three correct]

  c) A *[1 mark]*

  d) i) E.g. the rate at which a radioactive source decays *[1 mark]*. Its unit is the becquerel/Bq *[1 mark]*.

    ii)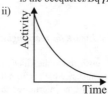
[1 mark for activity decreasing over time, 1 mark for correct shape of the graph]

  e) The time taken for the activity to halve *[1 mark]*.

8 a)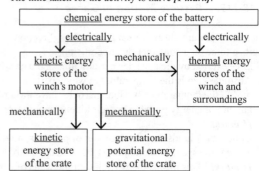
[4 marks for all correct, otherwise 3 marks for five correct, or 2 marks for three or four correct, or 1 mark for one or two correct]

  b) $\Delta GPE = m \times g \times \Delta h = 40.0 \times 10 \times 1.1 =$ **440 J**
[4 marks for correct answer, otherwise 1 mark for correct equation, 1 mark for correct substitution, 1 mark for correctly recalling the value of g]

9 a) i) $\rho = m \div V$ *[1 mark]*

    ii) Volume of water displaced = volume of the cube submerged
Volume = $0.1 \times 0.1 \times 0.07 = 0.0007$ m³
$m = \rho \times V = 1000 \times 0.0007 =$ **0.7 kg**
[3 marks for the correct answer, otherwise 1 mark for correct volume calculation, 1 mark for correct substitution to calculate mass]

  b) Area of the cube's face: $0.1 \times 0.1 = 0.01$ m²
$P = F \div A = 7 \div 0.01 =$ **700 Pa**
[4 marks for correct answer, otherwise 1 mark for correct area calculation, 1 mark for correct equation, 1 mark for correct substitution]

10 a) Independent variable: Roughness of surface *[1 mark]*.
Dependent variable: Deceleration / speed of trolley *[1 mark]*.

  b) i) Assuming that all of the energy in the spring's elastic potential energy store is transferred to the trolley's kinetic energy store:
$KE = \frac{1}{2} \times m \times v^2 = 0.5 \times 0.50 \times 0.60^2 = 0.09$, so
energy in the spring's elastic potential energy store = **0.09 J**
[3 marks for correct answer, otherwise 1 mark for equating energy in elastic potential and kinetic energy stores, 1 mark for correct substitution]

    ii) $v^2 - u^2 = 2 \times a \times x$
$a = (v^2 - u^2) \div 2x$
$= (0.40^2 - 0.60^2) \div (2 \times 1.00) = -0.1$
So deceleration = **0.1 m/s²**
[3 marks for the correct answer, otherwise 1 mark for rearranging the equation and 1 mark for correct substitution]

c) Momentum before collision = momentum after collision
Before the collision:
First trolley: $p = m \times v = 0.50 \times 0.60 = 0.30$
Second trolley: $p = 0$
After the collision:
First trolley: $p = 0$
Second trolley: $p = m \times v = 0.30$
$0.40 \times v = 0.30$, so $v = 0.30 \div 0.40 = $ **0.75 m/s**
[4 marks for correct answer, otherwise 1 mark for correct equation, 1 mark for correctly calculating the momentum before collision, 1 mark for equating this to the momentum after the collision and correctly rearranging for velocity]

11 a) E.g.

[1 mark for filament lamps and resistor in series with each other, 1 mark for motor in parallel with other components, 1 mark for correct placement of switches, 2 marks for all circuit symbols correctly drawn, otherwise 1 mark for 4 symbols correctly drawn]

b) E.g. as current flows through both the resistor and the motor, the charges do work against resistance *[1 mark]*. This causes energy to be transferred electrically to the thermal energy stores of the resistor and the motor *[1 mark]*. The motor also does work against friction (as it is moving) which causes energy to be transferred mechanically to the thermal energy store of the motor *[1 mark]*. A way to reduce this heating would be to lubricate the moving parts inside the motor *[1 mark]*.

c) $E = V \times I \times t = 6.0 \times (70 \times 10^{-3}) \times (10 \times 60) = 252$ J
$3 \text{ g} = 3 \div 1000 = 0.003$ kg
$\Delta Q = m \times c \times \Delta\theta = 0.003 \times 400 \times 25 = 30$ J
$252 - 30 = 222$ J = **220 J (to 2 s.f.)**
[5 marks for correct answer, otherwise 1 mark for correctly stating $E = VIt$, 1 mark for correctly substituting into this equation, 1 mark for correct substitution into $\Delta Q = mc\Delta\theta$, 1 mark for both energies correctly calculated]

12 a) E.g. electrons in insulators are not free to move *[1 mark]* so a static charge can be built up on them *[1 mark]*.

b) As the belt brushes past comb A, the comb pulls electrons off the belt *[1 mark]*, making it positively charged *[1 mark]*. The positively charged belt then brushes past comb B, pulling electrons off the comb *[1 mark]*. This makes comb B, and therefore the dome, positively charged *[1 mark]*.

c) i) Electrons have moved from the earthed metal to the dome *[1 mark]*.
ii) Convert the potential difference to V:
320 kV × 1000 = 320 000 V
Convert the charge to C:
15 μC ÷ 10^6 = 0.000015 C
$E = Q \times V = 0.000015 \times 320\,000 = $ **4.8 J**
[4 marks for correct answer, otherwise 1 mark for correct conversion of all units, 1 mark for correct equation, 1 mark for correct substitution]

13 a) E.g. some radiation is reflected or absorbed by the Earth's atmosphere *[1 mark]*.

b) It gets cooler *[1 mark]*. The intensity and distribution of the radiation emitted by an object depends on its temperature *[1 mark]*. As an object cools, the peak wavelength emitted becomes longer, so objects appear redder *[1 mark]*.

c) i) E.g. visible / UV / X-ray / gamma region *[1 mark]*.
ii) The total mass of the nuclei that undergo nuclear fusion is higher than the mass of the products of nuclear fusion *[1 mark]*. As more nuclei fuse, the mass of the star decreases, so the astronomer is correct *[1 mark]*.

d) Planet B is more massive/has a larger mass than planet A, so at a given distance from its surface *[1 mark]*, its gravitational field strength is larger *[1 mark]*. This means that the centripetal force acting on the satellite around planet B is larger than the force acting on the satellite around planet A *[1 mark]*, so the satellite around planet B must travel faster to remain in a stable orbit *[1 mark]*.

14 a) $\dfrac{V_s}{V_p} = \dfrac{N_s}{N_p}$
So $V_s = (V_p \times N_s) \div N_p = (25\,000 \times 16\,000) \div 1000$
$= 400\,000$ V
(For a 100% efficient transformer, power in = power out, so:)
$V_p \times I_p = V_s \times I_s$, so $I_s = (V_p \times I_p) \div V_s$
$I_s = (25\,000 \times 4000) \div 400\,000 = $ **250 A**
[4 marks for correct answer, otherwise 1 mark for correct substitution to find the p.d. across the secondary coil, 1 mark for correct p.d. across the secondary coil, 1 mark for correct substitution to find current through the secondary coil]

b) Power output of generator $= IV = 4000 \times 25\,000$
$= 1.0 \times 10^8$ W
Power input of generator
$P = E \div t = (34.92 \times 10^9) \div 60 = 5.82 \times 10^8$ W
efficiency $= \dfrac{\text{useful energy transferred}}{\text{total energy supplied}}$
$= 1.0 \times 10^8 \div 5.82 \times 10^8 = 0.1718...$
$= $ **17% (to 2 s.f.)**
[5 marks for correct answer given to a sensible number of significant figures, otherwise 1 mark for either correct power equation, 1 mark for correct power output, 1 mark for efficiency equation, 1 mark for correct power input]

15 a) As the plant generates electricity, energy is transferred mechanically *[1 mark]* from the gravitational potential energy store of the water to its kinetic energy store *[1 mark]*. This is transferred mechanically *[1 mark]* to the kinetic energy stores of the turbine and the generator *[1 mark]*. The energy is then transferred away from the power station electrically *[1 mark]*.

b) How to grade your answer:
Level 0: There is no relevant information. *[No marks]*
Level 1: There is a brief explanation of the safety implications of storing nuclear waste, with points not inked together. *[1-2 marks]*
Level 2: There is some explanation of the safety implications of storing nuclear waste with some reference to half-life. Some of the points made are linked together. *[3-4 marks]*
Level 3: There is a clear and detailed explanation of the safety implications caused by storing nuclear waste and of the precautions needed, including a reference to the penetrating and ionising power of the radiation produced and the half-life of the waste. The points made are well-linked and the answer has a clear and logical structure. *[5-6 marks]*
Here are some points your answer may include:
The caesium has a half-life of 30 years, so it will take 30 years for the activity of the caesium to halve.
This means that the surrounding area will be exposed to radiation for a long time.
The gamma rays released by the waste can travel a large distance before ionising an atom.
This means that a large area surrounding the nuclear waste will be irradiated.
Improper storage may also lead to nearby areas, e.g. streams, being contaminated.
Exposure to nuclear radiation is harmful to humans and other living creatures.
It can kill cells or cause gene mutations which can lead to cancer.
So nuclear waste should be stored far away from humans and other living creatures.
Shielding should also be put around the storage sites of nuclear waste to reduce irradiation.
Storage sites should be secure, to make sure the containers that hold the caesium cannot get damaged and leak.

Physics Equations Sheet

Here are some equations you might find useful when you're working through the book —
you'll be given these equations in the exams.

Section 1 — Motion and Forces

$v^2 - u^2 = 2 \times a \times x$	(final velocity)^2 – (initial velocity)^2 = 2 × acceleration × distance
$F = \dfrac{(mv - mu)}{t}$	force = change in momentum ÷ time

Make sure you understand all the equations on this page, and you're happy using and rearranging them.

Section 7 — Electricity and Circuits

$E = I \times V \times t$	energy transferred = current × potential difference × time

Section 8 — Electric and Magnetic Fields

$F = B \times I \times l$	force on a conductor at right angles to a magnetic field carrying a current = magnetic flux density × current × length
$\dfrac{V_p}{V_s} = \dfrac{N_p}{N_s}$	$\dfrac{\text{potential difference across primary coil}}{\text{potential difference across secondary coil}} = \dfrac{\text{number of turns in primary coil}}{\text{number of turns in secondary coil}}$
$V_p \times I_p = V_s \times I_s$	potential difference across primary coil × current in primary coil = potential difference across secondary coil × current in secondary coil (for transformers with 100% efficiency)

Section 9 — Matter

$\Delta Q = m \times c \times \Delta\theta$	change in thermal energy = mass × specific heat capacity × change in temperature
$Q = m \times L$	thermal energy for a change of state = mass × specific latent heat
$P_1 \times V_1 = P_2 \times V_2$	pressure at volume 1 × volume 1 = pressure at volume 2 × volume 2 (for a fixed mass of gas at a constant temperature)
$E = \frac{1}{2} \times k \times x^2$	energy transferred in stretching = 0.5 × spring constant × (extension)^2
$P = h \times \rho \times g$	pressure due to a column of liquid = height of column × density of liquid × gravitational field strength

PEQ42B